A PRACTICAL GUIDE TO

Survival

by Victoria Mason

WHAT TO DO BEFORE, DURING AND AFTER DISASTERS IN THE HOME

Illustrated by: Sally Kay Narramore
                  Derek Edgar
Research Assistant: Donna Kay Heredia
Editorial Services: Gene Du Pont
Cover design/Logos: Robert James Design

Mason Publications

First Printing – December 1986

Typesetting and Layout by Victoria Graphics
Printed in the United States by KNI Inc.

ISBN No. 0-941153-00-2

Published by Mason Publications
P. O. Box 4974
Orange, CA 92618-4974

YOUR EMERGENCY PHONE NUMBERS-

Emergency Services

PARAMEDICS · 911 or _____
FIRE DEPARTMENT · 911 or _____
POLICE DEPARTMENT · 911 or _____
EMERGENCY AMBULANCE · 911 or _____
FAMILY DOCTOR _____
FAMILY DENTIST _____
POISON CONTROL CENTER _____
NEAREST HOSPITAL _____

Personal Emergency Information

Father's Work No. _____
Mother's Work No. _____
Children's School No.(s) _____
_____
_____

Neighbor(s) Name _____ Phone _____
    Name _____ Phone _____
    Name _____ Phone _____
Family member/close friend in other area for disaster
check-in point._____
Insurance Agent _____
Gas Company _____
Electric Company _____
Water Company _____
Red Cross Disaster/Information No. _____
Veterinarian _____
Miscellaneous _____

ACKNOWLEDGEMENTS

I never realized how difficult it would be to write the acknowledgments until I tried to thank all of the people who had contributed their time and efforts. There were so many that contributed 'a lot or a little,' and every bit necessary for the completion.

A few that must be mentioned are Donna Kay Heredia as research assistant, errand person "go-fer" and all round helper; Don who was there for support, suggestions, an appreciation of the finer points, hard work, unending hours, not to mention that he's the best brother anyone ever had; Sally, for her artistic talent, imagination, understanding, patience, hard work, and innumerable hours; Gene for his editorial and publishing knowledge, research, assistance, patience, hard work, and ungodly hours; Val 'cause she's my twin; Byron for his patience; and Dave for his support. Without their efforts this would have forever been 'in the works.'

Others who contributed their time and expertise and deserve special thanks are: Gordon West, WB6NOA, West Coast Amateur Radio School; Scott Brown and Jose Valbuena, Paramedics, Orange County Fire Department; Judy Dufort and Lynn Forrester, Crime Prevention-Orange Police Department; Cheryl A. Bode, Orange County Sexual Assault Network; Wally Benson, Captain, San Diego Fire Department.

DEDICATION

To the Cadets of Lucky Troop 13, Long Beach Girl Scout Council, where this all began;

To Dad and Winifred to make amends for my neglect while writing this book;

And to my grandson Grant, who's first birthday marks it's completion.

All of the emergency procedures contained in this guide have been researched, compiled, and edited from a wide variety of authoritative sources. Included, principally are:

California Office of the Attorney General
City of Orange Fire Department
City of Orange Police Department-Crime Prevention
Civil Defense
National Oceanic and Atmospheric Administration (NOAA)
National Science Foundation-U.S. Antarctic Research Program
National Weather Service
Orange County Fire Department
Orange County Sexual Assault Network (OCSAN)
Office of Emergency Services
Saddleback Search and Rescue Team, Inc.
San Diego Fire Department
U.S. Food and Drug Administration
U.S. Geological Survey
University of California, Berkeley
University of California, Irvine

PREFACE

This book contains information that is primarily designed to:

- Make you aware of the emergency situations that COULD HAPPEN TO YOU.

- Familiarize you with the nature of some of the disasters that do occur.

- Help you plan ahead so you will be ready should any of these emergencies arise.

- Teach you what to do during any given emergency or disaster situation as it occurs.

- Teach you how to survive after the emergency situation until you, your family, home, and community are back to normal.

TABLE OF CONTENTS

RECIPE FOR SURVIVAL

Start with a cool, calm attitude
Add some common sense
A dash of humor
and a survival plan for YOU.
Mix with first aid training
Your personal SURVIVAL CACHE™ - filled,
and the knowhow to use it.
And don't forget this guide, it will come in handy too.

YIELD: a family of survivors

Viki Mason

INTRODUCTION

BASIC INFORMATION
BEFORE
DURING
AFTER
HOW TO REPORT AN EMERGENCY CORRECTLY
INSURANCE

INTRODUCTION

BASIC INFORMATION

During any disaster of major proportions, you cannot expect to receive outside assistance for at least three days and possibly longer. Only the most critical elements of rescue and survival will be taken care of immediately. Therefore, you will be responsible for the maintenance and well being of yourself and your family until outside help becomes available.

The information contained in this section is an accumulation of procedures that will apply to most emergency situations. In the following chapters you will find expanded and precise informa-tion pertaining to particular emergencies.

BEFORE

Emergency preparedness means preparing for an emergency. It doesn't necessarily mean you are going to have one. It just means that you will be ready in the event something ever does happen. Use this book as a guide to help you prepare ahead of time for any emergency, natural or otherwise, that may arise. By doing this you and your family will greatly increase your chances of survival and your ability to get back to your normal living situation quickly and with the least amount of inconvenience.

- Maintain a minimum supply of food and water sufficient for your whole family for at least 2 weeks. Many sources suggest a 2 to 3-day supply of food and water, but we feel that the longer period will ensure that you have enough. It is also important to rotate you stock of food as required through your regular meals. See Section FOOD for list of foods' shelf life.

- Keep your automobile fueled. If electric power is cut off, filling stations may not be able to operate pumps for several days. But, DO NOT STORE gasoline.

- Have family members learn disaster plans for schools and for companies employing them.

- Arrange for a family member outside of the area to be an "information center" for the welfare and location of family members in your area.

- Have complete lists of all possessions (backed up with photographs), including serial and model numbers, on file on the premises and a duplicate set off the premises in a safe place, such as a safe deposit box, a relative, etc.

You will need to replace the following documents if lost, damaged, or stolen:

- auto registration and title
- bank books
- birth certificates
- credit cards
- driver's license
- income tax records
- insurance policies
- marriage and divorce papers
- military discharge papers
- passports
- pre-paid burial contracts
- social security cards
- stocks and bonds
- title to deeds
- warranties
- wills

- Keep immunizations up to date for all family members.

- Have extra prescription medicines and eyeglasses in storage; drug stores may be closed for several days and your doctor unreachable.

READ THIS BOOK NOW AT YOUR LEISURE. Add notes or pointers that pertain to your particular situation should you ever have to cope with a disaster.

DURING

During an emergency situation you may become alarmed, frightened, apprehensive, disoriented, terrified, and/or afraid for yourself and your family. You may be all of these things, that's normal. BUT, YOU CANNOT ALLOW YOURSELF TO PANIC.

Your survival in any given emergency will depend on your ability to figure out the problem and take the correct action. How you react during an emergency is the key to your survival. You have to stay calm. You cannot lose your ability to reason.

REMEMBER — PANIC CAN KILL

Learn how to keep yourself and your family safe DURING and IMMEDIATELY AFTER an emergency while the initial danger is still present.

Your priorities are, in order of importance:

air
escape from immediate danger
medical help
shelter
water
food.

The most important factors that will govern your actions are emotional control (staying calm) and proper attitude. Your mind holds all the information you need, but if you cannot control yourself this knowledge is useless.

- ALWAYS MAINTAIN A GOOD ATTITUDE. This will keep you going longer than food and water.

- Tune radios to local Emergency Broadcast System stations for information, damage reports, and instructions.

- Follow your emergency plan to protect yourself and your family. Your emergency plan was set up while everything was normal and you were thinking calmly and rationally. DON'T CHANGE IT NOW WHEN EVERYTHING IS GOING TO HELL AND YOU ARE EXCITED AND NOT THINKING CLEARLY.

AFTER

With the supplies you have prepared ahead of time, and through the guidance of this book, you will be able to begin the everyday struggle of living under other than normal conditions after the emergency is over.

The correct actions you should take in a particular emergency situation are listed under each chapter. By following our directions for preparing ahead, you are already halfway there. So, when a disaster strikes or the emergency arrives, you will already know what to do. It's just a matter of following through with the planning you started.

- Keep an extra flashlight, first aid kit, battery powered transistor radio with extra batteries in the home, ready for use at any time. The best places to keep these items are in the bedroom closets, on headboards, near or under beds. Check them periodically to be sure that they are in good working condition. Mark your radio at your emergency frequencies.

 You can extend the life of your extra batteries by storing them in your refrigerator.

Also, fire extinguisher(s) are an important item to have handy. Be sure all responsible family members know where they are kept and how to use them.

- Teach responsible members of your family how to turn the utilities on and off at their main sources. See Section UTILITIES

- Conduct family discussions about possible disasters. Plan your emergency survival cache, evacuation routes, and designated safe meeting places.

- Conduct home hazard inspections at least every six months. Correct hazards.

- Teach responsible members how to call for help.

- Check for injuries to your family. Do not attempt to move seriously injured persons unless they are in immediate danger of further injury.

- If unable to contact the fire department for emergency medical treatment, go to the nearest hospital. First aid as well as food, shelter, and clothing will also be available at all Red Cross shelters.

- Check for hazards such as fire, gas leaks, that would put you in immediate danger and evacuate to predesignated safe area if necessary.

- Check neighbors for injuries, especially those who have difficulty getting around.

- Check your emergency supplies to evaluate their survival. If any hazard is still present that can cause damage, move to a safer area. Immediately clean up spilled medicines, drugs, and other potentially harmful materials.

- Confine pets if walls or fences are down.

- Wear shoes in all areas near debris or broken glass.

- Contact your local disaster agency or the Red Cross for any needed assistance.

- Information concerning the welfare or location of separated family members will be handled by the Red Cross. Contact them instead of the police or fire departments for this information.

- Contact your insurance agent as soon as possible and try to compile as comprehensive a list as possible of all losses.

- Report broken utility lines to appropriate authorities.

- Do not spread rumors. They often do great harm following disasters.

Evacuation

- Plan a variety of evacuation routes that deal with the threats of different disasters. In an actual emergency, listen to the Emergency Broadcast System on the radio for possible designated routes. If you have to evacuate:

  A. Prominently post a message indicating where you can be found.

  B. Take with you:
     - ✓ Medicines and first aid kit.
     - ✓ Flashlight, radio and extra batteries/bulbs.
     - ✓ Important papers and cash.
     - ✓ Food, sleeping bags/blankets and extra clothes.
     - ✓ Make arrangements for pets.

  C. Do respond to requests for help from police, fire fighters, civil defense, and Red Cross. Cooperate fully with public safety officials.

HOW TO REPORT AN EMERGENCY CORRECTLY

When a fire or other emergency occurs, it is very easy to get excited, BUT DON'T. To think clearly you MUST STAY CALM. If you're excited and unable to talk clearly, no one will be able to understand you and this will delay getting help to your location.

Make sure that each member of your family knows what number to call to contact the fire and police or sheriff's department. Post emergency phone numbers near each phone.

If you have to make an emergency call:

STOP

**TAKE 3 LONG EASY DEEP BREATHS
AND LET THEM OUT SLOWLY!
Plan ahead what information you must tell them.
Above all, STAY CALM, DO NOT PANIC.**

When reporting an emergency, tell the dispatcher:

1.   WHAT KIND OF EMERGENCY (fire, medical aid, etc.)

2.   WHERE: STREET NAME AND NUMBER, include north, south, east, or west if applicable, APARTMENT BUILDING, UNIT and CITY. The name of the complex is also helpful.

3.   STOP TALKING and LISTEN, dispatcher will ask the questions.

   Information you will need:

   • Nearest cross street to emergency address.
   • Phone Number you are calling from.
   • Other immediate medical details

- Your name

- Any other information pertinent to the emergency.

4. STAY ON THE LINE to answer any questions. DO NOT HANG UP the phone until the person to whom you are speaking hangs up first.

5. SPEAK SLOWLY AND CLEARLY; hurrying causes mistakes and misunderstandings.

6. TURN YOUR PORCH LIGHT ON, if possible, or a next door neighbors.

7. HAVE SOMEONE at the street TO GUIDE THE EMERGENCY VEHICLE to the scene when they arrive.

It is required in most areas that your address be posted in a conspicuous place, easily readable from the street. (Address numerals should be at least three inches in height.)

INSURANCE

Check your insurance policy and your carrier. Are you adequately covered in case of a disaster?

For example: An earthquake causes a dam to break which floods your home causing damage . . . . Does your earthquake insurance cover the damage caused by the flooding or do you also need flood insurance? Be sure of the exact coverage of your current insurance and modify it according to your needs.

For your protection, carry sufficient and appropriate insurance, i.e., homeowner's, renter's, fire, flood, and earthquake. Check with your insurance agent for your personal requirements. *NOTE:* Landlords only insure contents that they own.

Insurance companies continually upgrade policy coverage to encompass disasters.

If you are not insured or your insurance does not cover your losses, some or all of your losses can be deducted on your Federal Income Tax.

Earthquake Insurance — Various types of earthquake and other disaster insurance policies are offered by many insurance companies.

If you live in any area where there is a potential for a specific disaster or disasters, your best protection is the proper insurance to cover any losses that might incur.

NOTES

CRIME PREVENTION

CRIME PREVENTION

Crimes happen all of the time — At any time of the day or night — To any person — at any place. It is up to you, the individual person, to take precautions to protect yourself and your property. To lessen the chance of being a victim you must constantly be alert to what is happening in your immediate surroundings at all times and to have some idea of what to do to protect yourself or property under any circumstances.

Just remember that old adage: Better safe than sorry.....

With the assistance of the Crime Prevention Center, Office of the Attorney General, Sacramento, California, Crime Prevention — Orange Police Department, and the Orange County Sexual Assault Network (OCSAN), we are able to provide the following information.

PERSONAL PROTECTION

Avoid becoming a victim of a crime when you are out and about or working at your job. By taking a few simple precautions, you can reduce the risk to yourself, and also discourage those who commit crimes.

 BE PREPARED — Always be alert and aware of the people around you.

Educate yourself concerning prevention tactics.

ON THE STREET

- Be aware of locations and situations which would make you vulnerable to crime.

- Walk confidently and at a steady pace.

- Make eye contact with people when walking.

- Know and practice self-defense tactics.

- Be alert to your surroundings and the people around you — especially if you are alone or it is dark.

- Walking alone at night can be hazardous. If you must walk at night, walk on well lighted streets, avoiding shrubbery and other places of concealment.

- Whenever possible, travel with a friend.

- Stay in well-lighted areas as much as possible.

- Walk close to the curb. Avoid doorways, bushes and alleys where someone could hide. Walk out and as far away from them as you can with safety.

- If you carry a purse, your personal safety might depend on **not** clinging to it. Although a purse snatcher's intent is to steal the purse, the grabbing and shoving that may take place may result in your being injured.

- Carry a shoulder bag securely between your arm and your body. Carry a clutch bag unsnapped and upside down between your arm and your body with the wallet in a zipper compartment. If someone attempts to steal your purse, loosen your grip — thus allowing the contents to fall to the ground.

- If you carry an item as a weapon (e.g., keys, pen, whistle, etc.), walk with it in your hand — not in your purse or pocket.

- Do not respond to conversation from strangers on the street — continue walking.

- If a car pulls up slowly or bothers you, cross the street and walk or run in the other direction.

- If you feel someone is following you, turn around and check. Proceed to the nearest lighted house or place of business.

- Don't overburden yourself with bags or packages which might impede running or taking care of yourself.

- Wear clothes and shoes that give you freedom of movement.

- If you feel you are in danger, don't be afraid to scream and run.

- Carry a whistle or freon horn.

- Carry as little cash as possible.

- Don't hitchhike.

- Hold your purse tightly, close to your body. Keep your wallet in a front or buttoned hip pocket.

- Be careful when people stop you for directions or information. Always reply from a distance, and never get too close to the car.

- When walking to your house or car, have your key in your hand, ready, to prevent any unnecessay delays. If you are ever followed, getting away fast, changing directions and walking into a crowded, well lighted area is best.

CAR SAFETY

- Always lock car doors after entering or leaving your car.

- Park in well-lighted areas.

- Have your car keys in your hand so you don't have to linger before entering your car.

  –Keys can also serve as a possible weapon against an attacker.

- Always check the back seat before entering a car.

- If you think you are being followed, drive to a public place or a police station.

- Don't stop to aid disabled motorists. Go to a phone and request help for them.

- If your car breaks down, use distress signals such as putting the hood up, a white flag (piece of cloth) on the aerial, or emergency flashers. Remain in the car with the doors locked. Wait for the police or ask strangers who do stop to send a tow truck or police back for you. Be wary of accepting help from strangers.

- If someone threatens you while you are in your car, lock all doors and blow the horn in short bursts to attract attention.

- If you are followed by another car, put your hand on the horn all the way to the nearest gas, police, or fire station or lighted home. Or use any other method to draw attention to your car.

- Keep your car in good working order with sufficient gasoline.

- Lock your car doors when driving.

- Do not pick up hitchhikers.

WHILE WAITING FOR A BUS

- Try to avoid isolated bus stops.
  Stand away from the curb until bus arrives.

- Don't open your purse or wallet while boarding the bus — have your pass or money already in your hand.

- Don't invite trouble — keep gold chains out of sight; don't flash your jewelry; and turn your rings around so the stones don't show.

ON BOARD BUSES

- During off hours, ride as near to the driver as possible.

- Stay alert — and beware of the people around you.

- If someone bothers you, change seats and/or tell the driver.

- Carry your wallet inside your coat, or in a front pocket. A comb, placed horizontally in the fold of your wallet, will alert you if someone tries to remove it from your pocket.

- Keep your handbag in front of you and hold it close to your body with both hands.

- Check your purse or wallet if someone is jostling, crowding or pushing you.

- If you see any suspicious activity, tell the driver.

IN AN ELEVATOR

- Check elevator interior before entering. Wait until the next elevator if you are uncertain of any occupant.

- If you are in an elevator with another person, stand near the control panel. If attacked, press the alarm and as many of the control buttons as possible.

- Be alert to pickpockets on crowded elevators.

OFFICE SECURITY

- Never leave your purse or billfold in plain view or in the pocket of a jacket hanging on a door or rack.

- Personal property should be marked with your drivers license number.

- If you work alone or before/after normal business hours, keep the office door locked.

- If you work late, try to find another worker or a security guard to walk out with you.

- Report all suspicious persons and activities to the proper authorities (office manager, building security, law enforcement).

- Be aware of escape routes for emergancies and post the police and fire department numbers near telephones.

SENIOR CITIZENS

- Have social security or retirement checks sent directly to your checking or savings account.

- Beware of "get rich quick" scams or persons who ask you to give them large sums of money.

TELEPHONE

- Don't give information about yourself to strangers over the phone or admit that you are alone.

- You can list your name and number in the phone book without your address.

- Keep all emergency numbers near the telephone.

- Hang up on obscene phone callers.

- If obscene phone caller persists and keeps calling back, notify your telephone company.

  You can blow a whistle into the receiver which may inhibit the caller's desire to phone back.

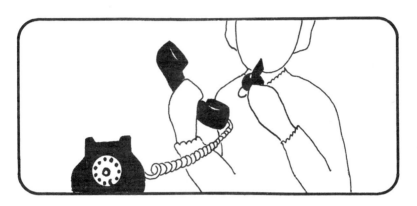

SEXUAL ASSAULT/RAPE

Sexual Assault/Rape like other disasters is the direct cause of an outside force. And the aftermath can be more devastating than any other. The disruption of the lifestyle of the victim and the family members along with the accompanying emotional problems can last for a short time or for a lifetime.

The F.B.I. states that *rape is the most frequently committed violent crime* in the U.S. today, surpassing murder, robbery and other assaults. Rape is a crime by an outsider against a victim — not invited or instigated by the victim (male as well as female). One of the great problems connected with sexual assault/rape is the attitudes of the people involved, from those first in contact with the victim to the victim herself. Through the efforts of many people (mostly volunteers) across the country, RAPE CRISIS HOTLINES have been set up and the crime of rape is being brought out of the closet and recognized for what it really is, an act of violation and victimization.

MYTHS and FACTS

The following are some of the most common myths concerning sexual assault/rape and their truth in fact.

MYTH: Rape is a non-violent crime.
. . . .
FACT: RAPE IS A VIOLENT CRIME, usually committed under the threat of great bodily injury or death. In fact, 87% of all rapists either threaten the victim with violence or carry a weapon. Nearly all women who call a rape hotline state that their worst fear during the assault was that they were going to be killed.

MYTH: The primary motive for rape is sexual.
. . . .
FACT: RAPE IS AN ACT OF VIOLENCE ACTED OUT SEXUALLY. It is not an act of sex. Two-thirds of all rapists already have "sex" available to them. Men who rape are motivated by a need to dominate, humiliate, control, brutalize, and have power over another human being.

MYTH: It could never happen to me.
. . . .
FACT: IT CAN HAPPEN TO YOU! Anyone can be a victim regardless of gender, age, appearance, ethnicity, income level, and lifestyle. Reported victims range in age from under 1 year to over 90 years old. Some statistics from California: Orange County – 1 out of every 4 women will be sexually assaulted, and Los Angeles – 1 in 3 women. And not just women—the crisis hotlines report that more men have started calling in as victims. But, as they will not officially report their assaults it is difficult to project the actual number of male victims.

MYTH: You can only be "RAPED" by a stranger – forced sex among acquaintances is not rape.
. . . .

FACT: WOMEN HAVE THE RIGHT TO SAY 'NO'! "Forced Sex" is just a misleading, inaccurate term which denies this fact. *'DATE* (acquaintance) *RAPES'* are just as devastating, if not more so, than *'STRANGER RAPES'* because the victim has trusted her safety to a person she knows, and that trust is betrayed when she is raped. In an estimated 60-80% of all sexual assaults the victim knows her assailant. And, the victim of an "acquaintance rape" more readily believes that she is responsible for the assault, therefore will not talk about it to others; and so for her, the emotional trauma is prolonged.

MYTH: Rapists are psychotic or "sick" men.

. . . .

FACT: ONLY 3% OF ALL CONVICTED RAPISTS ARE DIAGNOSED CLINICALLY AS PSYCHOTIC. In a comparison study between convicted rapists and persons convicted of other criminal charges, there was NO difference in personality profiles except for the tendency of the convicted rapists to show more overt aggression, condone the use of violence towards women and to strongly ascribe to traditional sex-role stereotypes. Rapists can be and are husbands, fathers, doctors, lawyers, police officers, school teachers, and the "all-American-boy-next door."

MYTH: Women who are raped are "asking for it."

. . . .

FACT: OVER 50% OF ALL RAPES OCCUR WITHIN A WOMAN'S OWN HOME— a woman in her home is hardly asking to be assaulted! Rape is not related to a woman's provocative dress or her manner, evidenced by the fact that babies in diapers and fully-clothed grandmothers are victims of rape. Although women are *expected* to be attractive in our society, they suddenly are made to blame for a rapist's actions if they are attractive to "the wrong person at the wrong time." When a woman takes the time to make herself attractive, she is seeking approval and acceptance–not victimization! When a jeweler displays a diamond in a store window, he is asking that it be appreciated, not stolen.

MYTH: Rape is impossible without a woman's consent, and she is hurt only if she's beaten.

. . . .

FACT: ANYONE CAN BE IMMOBILIZED BY FEAR – of violent threats or the threat of death aimed at themselves or their love ones. 87% of all rapists use some type of physical force, with and without a weapon. Added to the threat of bodily injury are fear, guilt, shame, disgust and the physical traumas of possible V.D., pregnancy or internal injuries.

MYTH: Rape is over in a few minutes.

. . . .

FACT: AN AVERAGE ASSAULT TIME IS OVER 4 HOURS (some last over a period of days), according to the Los Angeles Rape and Battering Hotline statistics. And, the victimization does not end when the rapist leaves—the physical and emotional trauma can last indefinitely.

WHAT TO DO IF YOU ARE. . .

A Victim.

Your options are:

1) call your **Rape Crisis Hotline** and/or

2) call the police, or

3) call the paramedics, ambulance, medical help

4) do nothing.

Option 1

Rape Crisis Hotline (24-hour) is staffed by concerned citizens, past victims of sexual assault and other volunteers, all trained Sexual Assault Victim Specialists. They are there to provide comfort, counseling, information on available resources and help. A trained counselor will go with the victim to the hospital, police station, court, district attorney's office and any other required visit. You will not be alone.

The Hotline for your area should be listed in the front pages of your telephone book under Rape Crisis Hotline or Sexual Assault.

Option 2

In any crime the police must be notified as soon as possible so data, evidence, any pertinent information can be recovered and the criminal caught. Granted, on the face of it, this might seem like an intimidating option. However, you have the right to have a supportive person present with you (i.e., a Hotline volunteer/advocate) to answer any questions or to make sure you are treated well. Benefits to reporting the assault to the police include possible prevention of repeat assaults by the attacker; possible financial assistance if your state has a victims assistance program; and finally, the benefit to you in taking your power back by acting on what has happened.

Option 3
   Many counties have paramedic programs (usually part of the fire department) where highly trained emergency medical personnel go to the victim, and then the victim is taken to the hospital. Or someone could take you to the hospital direct or to a doctor. Medical help is needed. The medical problems include more than just physical injuries — chance of pregnancy, diseases, infection are all things that may need treatment.

Option 4
   You do not have to do anything. But, do you really want to go through this alone? You are going to be hurting, both physically and emotionally, and that is nothing to go through alone. Emotionally you will be feeling fear, terror, shock, shame, embarrassment, guilt, frustration, helplessness, all kinds of emotions all mixed together. Added to this is the fear of getting pregnant or catching a disease. Talking about it HELPS! It breaks down the feelings of isolation you may be having, and will help you to heal faster.

No matter what your choice, you need not face this alone. You have been the victim of a crime and you deserve help. You need someone to talk to who will listen and understand your feelings, someone who can counsel and understand.

A Family Member or Friend.

It is normal for you to feel upset, confusion, anger, fear, guilt, frustration, a myriad of emotions that concern your feelings over what happened. But remember, you are the one she (or he) is counting on for support, physical and emotional.

There are four things you can do:

LISTEN — Let them tell you at their own pace what happened to them.
- You may ask questions to clarify the situation in your mind, but do not drill her for specific details.
- You may relate to her situation with something similar in your life, but only mention it briefly, never go on about yourself.

BE SUPPORTIVE
- Tell her you care about her and how she is feeling.
- Ask how she is feeling emotionally or how she is dealing with the incident. But again, don't drill her for information.
- Respond to any emotions that she is experienceing (i.e., fear, guilt, anger or embarrassment) as understandable and normal.
- Make time to help her find more professional help, or some other supportive individuals that she can call or see.
- Never make decisions for her, such as reporting to police.

 Never be critical or judgmental. Never say "That was a dumb or careless thing to do!" "You should have...," "Why didn't you...," or "I would have..." Never judge the victim or the situation.

EMOTIONAL and MEDICAL — Recognize that she needs professional care.
- Talk with her about emotional concerns - feelings and emotions about the attack, its impact on her life, relationships and behavior.
- Discuss her medical concerns - possibilities of physical and medical problems relating to the attack. The sooner they are recognized, the sooner they can be taken care of.

COMMUNITY RESOURCES – *Help her find them locally*

Communities all over the country are beginning to set up organizations to aid victims of rape, incest, and child molestation. For example, Orange County Sexual Assault Network (OCSAN) in Orange County, California, coordinates efforts to end sexual assault through community education and prevention programs. And, the State of California has set up a fund to aid sexual assault victims.

Other resources are:

✓   Rape Crisis Hotlines

✓   Victim of Crime Assistance Programs

✓   County Department of Mental Health

✓   Medical facilities (private doctors to Free Clinics)

✓   Women's Centers at Colleges or Universities.

In Seattle, Washington, a group of men have formed **Men Against Rape**, an organization to combat rape with education and confrontation of sexist behavior. They suggest a few points for the individual man to follow in order to create a non-threatening, safe environment for women:

●   Be aware of your own behavior which may be threatening to women – For example: on a quiet street at night, instead of walking behind a woman, cross to the other side.

●   Do not confuse mere friendliness with sexual invitation.

●   When appropriate, educate women friends about the possibility of potential rape.

●   Especially important – Be alert to signs of women (and men) who may be suffering physical or verbal assault and be willing to investigate and intervene.

Parts of the above section were reprinted with permission from the Laguna Beach Community Clinic, Laguna Beach, California, and the University of California, Irvine, Rape Prevention and Education Program.

HOME SECURITY

SOME DO'S AND DON'TS OF CRIME PREVENTION

- Secure all outside doors with deadbolt locks. Outer doors should be solid core wood (1 ¾ inches thick) or metal. Do not rely on chain locks.

- Place metal rods, wooden rods or broom handle in track of sliding glass doors.

- Use secure locks on windows. Put nails in window frames to allow windows to be opened during warm weather, yet maintain security.

- Have good lighting at all entrances.

- Never automatically open your door. Make sure you know who is at the door before you open it. Insist on identification from repair and sales persons, or anyone else you don't know. If in doubt, call their company for identification. You do not have to let anyone in.

- Installing and using a door viewer will prevent ever having to open your door to a stranger.

- Do not hide spare keys. Give your keys to trusted neighbors or friends.

- Have your locks rekeyed if you move into a new house or apartment.

- Do not admit persons asking to use your telephone. If you feel its an emergency, you can offer to make the call for them.

- Know your neighbors and their routines, and work out a mutual watch and warning system to prevent burglaries and other break-ins.

- Use automatic timers to turn indoor lights on and off to give the appearance you are at home.

- Stop mail and other deliveries when you leave for vacation.

- If you live in an apartment, be attentive and careful if you are alone in the laundry room or garage by yourself, especially late at night.

- If you live alone, listing only your last name and first initial in phone directories and on mailboxes is a wise practice.

- Having good locks to secure your doors and windows *and using them* every time you leave your home will prevent any unwelcome visitors.

- Be alert to protect your neighbor as well as yourself. Don't mention to a stranger that a neighbor lives alone or is home alone, it could cause serious problems.

- Identify your belongings by engraving an identifying number on your possessions.

- Check your neighborhood for things that might contribute to crime like poor street lighting, abandoned cars, vacant lots littered with debris, or boarded-up buildings.

Start your prevention program from the outside and work your way in — just as a burglar would.

YOUR FIRST LINE OF DEFENSE

Walls can have a place in crime prevention. However, fences and shrubbery can make good hiding places for burglars. The key is to keep trespassers out while keeping your property visible. Use picket or chain link fences, or hedges no more than waist high. that way you will form a barricade but everything that goes on inside is clearly visible.

ON THE OUTSIDE LOOKING IN

Burglars try the easiest entries first — doors and windows. If your doors or windows can't be quickly pried open, chances are the burglars will move on.

DOORS

- *LOCKS.* The best locks are deadbolt locks with a minimum 1 inch throw bolt containing a hardened steel insert which resists sawing. The strike plate should be attached to the door frame with screws that measure 4 inches. The double cylinder deadbolt lock requires a key to open from either side. This prevents burglars from breaking glass in the door and reaching through to turn the knob from inside. It also prevents them from exiting through the door if they've entered through some other means. Make sure the cylinder of the lock has a steel guard —

a ring around the key section. The cylinder guard should be tapered or rotate around the key section (if twisted) to prevent wrenching.

 Remember that a double cylinder deadbolt can also block your exit in an emergency. When locking the deadbolt WHEN YOU ARE INSIDE, it's best to leave the key in the lock.

Check with your local law enforcement agency or building inspector to see if these locks are permitted in your area.

- **HINGES.** If your doors swing out, the hinges are on the outside. A burglar can easily remove the hinge pins and lift the door out. To foil this, remove the center screw from each side of the hinge and insert a metal pin or headless screw on one side. When the door is closed, the end of the pin will fit into the opposite hole. That way even if the hinge pins are removed, the door will be bolted to the frame.

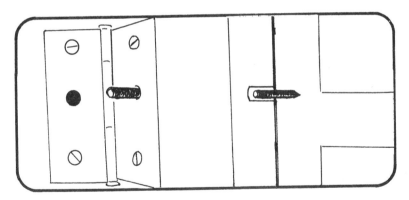

- **PADLOCKS.** Overhead doors, receiving doors, garage doors — all are typically secured with padlocks and hasps. Look for sturdy padlocks that don't release the key until the padlock is locked. That way you'll never leave a padlock unlocked. Remember that a padlock is only as good as the hasp it is mounted on. The hasp should be secured with bolts and mounted on a metal plate. Be sure bolts are concealed when the padlock is locked. And — make sure the padlock is case-hardened with a ⅜-inch shackle so it can resist repeated smashings.

- **DOOR CONSTRUCTION.** Burglars can virtually walk through a weak door. Hollow core doors should be replaced with solid core doors or strengthened with metal sheets. Replace weak door frames or reinforce them with steel or concrete. Glass in the door should be unbreakable safety glass. Glass also can be protected with steel bars or mesh, or by placing a polycarbonate sheet over the glass on the inside.

- **WINDOWS.** Protect windows by putting grates, grillwork, or bars over them. Or place clear polycarbonate sheets over the glass on the inside. Sheets should extend 1½ inches beyond the perimeter of the glass and be attached to a solid surface with bolts spaced approximately every 3 inches. Unbreakable safety glass is also available, but it is more expensive.

  Use key locks on all your windows and always keep them locked. But remember that even the best locks are useless if the window can be pried loose or the frame is rotten. If you need ventilation, open the windows, but not wide enough to allow an average adult to climb through. To secure the windows at that level, drill a slanted hole through the front window sash and part way through the back sash and insert a heavy duty nail or eyebolt.

- **OTHER ENTRANCES.** Skylights, ventilation ducts, and fire escapes may tempt a burglar because they are usually not visible from the street. Protect skylights and ducts with metal grates and iron bars. Outside fire escapes require special attention: the first stair should be too high for an adult to reach from the ground, and the door or window leading to the escape should be equipped with special emergency exit features. Window guards should be removable or hinged at the top or side to allow for emergency exit. Keys to locked windows or doors should be kept nearby for quick access.

IF A CRIME DOES OCCUR . . . REPORT IT!

Everyone should consider it his or her responsibility to report crime. Many criminals develop favorite areas for working, as well as predictable methods of operation. When you report all the facts about a crime it helps the police assign officers in the places where crimes are occuring or where they are most likely to occur.

At least one out of two crimes in the United States goes unreported, either because people don't think the police can do anything about it, or because people don't want to get involved. If you don't report crime, this allows the criminal to continue to operate without interference.

In many cases, it is the information provided by victims and witnesses that results in the arrest of a criminal. So tell the police as much as you can; no fact is too trivial. The police need the eyes and ears of all citizens.

And, again, remember: It's better to be safe than sorry!

IF YOU ARE THE VICTIM OF A BURGLARY

If you are burglarized, you can improve your chances of catching the thief and recovering your property by doing the following:

- If you return home or to your work and find a door or window has been forced open or broken while you were gone, or feel that something is wrong. *DON'T GO INSIDE. The burglar may still be there. Go to a neighbors and use their phone.*

- Call the police immediately to report the burglary. The sooner you contact the police the better their chances of solving your case.

- If you believe the burglar is still in the area, keep your premises under observation, if possible, so that you might be able to provide the Police with a description of a suspect or suspect vehicle.

- Don't *'CLEAN UP'* or disturb anything until the police arrive. You could destroy evidence that might help them.

- When the police officer arrives, tour the premises with him, and make a list of everything you know has been stolen. This will speed up the police report.

  In addition to the item name, include the brand name, model number, serial number (if any), estimated value, a full and complete description, and the driver's license or other I.D. number engraved on the item.

WHAT HAPPENS WHEN YOU CALL THE POLICE DEPARTMENT. . .

- Your call is dispatched by radio to a Patrol Officer assigned to your neighborhood.

  How soon the officer arrives depends on many factors. Other people from your neighborhood might be calling for police assistance at the same time. They follow a priority system, assigning the most urgent calls first.

  The following is a list of the categories and their priority, beginning with the most urgent:

  1. Incidents involving injury, bodily harm or threat to life;

  2. Reports of in-progress crimes/incidents not involving injury, or bodily harm or threat to life;

  3. Reports of all other crimes or incidents not in progress at time of call to police;

  4. Calls requesting other related police services.

- *A written report is taken*

  Once the officer arrives he will conduct a preliminary investigation and record the facts of the case and the action on a police report. This report is assigned a permanent number which will be your reference in any future calls to the police regarding this case.

HOW TO PREVENT FUTURE BURGLARIES

Encourage neighbors to:

- Have a block meeting on home security. Invite your Police Department's Crime Prevention Bureau. They will also help you set up a Neighborhood Watch Program.

- Have a personalized Home Security survey. These are done without charge by your Crime Prevention Bureau.

- Join Operation Identification

- Report ALL suspicious activity to your local Police Department.

EARTHQUAKE

EARTHQUAKE

An earthquake is the release of pressure in the earth's crust characterized by the shaking of the ground, the degree of which is dependent on the magnitude (strength) and location of the epicenter (the area of the earth's surface directly above the place of origin of an earthquake).

When we hear of the magnitude (severity) of an earthquake on the news, we are usually given a number between 1 and 9 on the Richter scale. This is a logarithmic scale and each whole number represents an increase in ground movement (amplitude) of 10 times, and a release of energy of about 31.5 times the preceeding whole number. Thus, an 8.3 magnitude earthquake is not twice as large as a shock of magnitude 4.3, but has 10,000 times as much ground movement, and releases almost 1 million times as much energy.

Due to certain physical principals in the earth itself, such as the breaking point of rock, an earthquake of a magnitude greater than 9 would be nearly impossible.

The following chart should give you some idea on how the numbers relate to the effects of the earthquake:

Magnitude Effects

1   Not felt. Picked up on instruments only.
2   Can barely be felt near the epicenter.
3   Can barely be felt. Causes no damage.
4   Can be felt a few miles from the epicenter, slight damage.

5	Causes some damage, felt by many.
6	Moderately destructive. Causes some severe damage.
7	Major destructive earthquake.
8+	Great earthquake.

There are many rumors about what will happen in a major earthquake. You have probably heard that California will fall into the ocean. This is literally impossible due to the physical characteristics of the earth. Another myth we can dispel here is that a number of small shocks will relieve the pressure build-up along a fault line and eliminate the possibility of a large earthquake. To relieve the pressure of an 8.5 magnitude earthquake, it would require about 1,000 shocks with the magnitude of 6.5 (about the size of the San Fernando Valley (1971) or Puget Sound (1965) earthquakes).

SYMPTOMS AND SIGNS

If you have never before experienced an earthquake, you may wonder what it feels like and what will happen. It is impossible to predict the sensations and effects of any given quake. It is pretty much dependent on the time (an earthquake can occur at any time), its location and your location, magnitude, and duration.

Some of the most common sensations can include:

- Hearing sounds that vary from a low rumbling noise to a loud banging around doors like they are being hit hard
- Hanging lamps, curtains, clothes on hangers, will start swinging
- Ground movement will vary from slight - slow moving to strong - abrupt shaking
- You may see ground movement - usually across open areas
- You may feel slightly dizzy, motion sickness

BEFORE AN EARTHQUAKE OCCURS

In many cases injuries from earthquakes are caused by something falling on you, be it debris or your favorite painting that's hanging over the couch. Most injuries and damage happen because those items, (like the painting) are in place and although hung or placed properly, may not be safe.

If you live in earthquake country, the risk of being injured in your own home, and damage to your home, can be minimized by following the procedures listed below.

SITE AND CONSTRUCTION

- Follow building codes to minimize earthquake hazards. We recommend that you exceed the codes because they may not be sufficient. Some research into site(s) and construction on your part first would be wise and would help protect your investment and life in the event of a major earthquake. Sites should be selected and engineered to reduce the hazards of earthquake damage. There is more information on this at the end of this chapter.

APPLIANCES

- If you have air conditioners, they should be placed at ground level along the side of your home or building. Be sure they are anchored solidly to the foundation or an anchor designed specifically for that. Do not place near a chimney or on the roof.

  If you have a window or wall air conditioner, be sure it is set on a well-braced shelf.

- If your refrigerator or any other heavy appliance or piece of furniture is on wheels or rollers, put casters or doorstops underneath to prevent them from rolling during the shaking.

- Use flexible lines and connections for water heaters and all gas appliances. There is an extreme hazard of explosion and fire from ruptured gas lines.

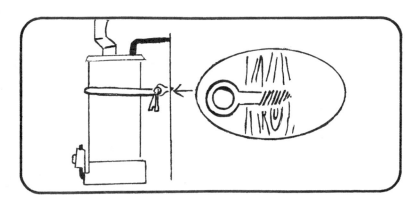

- Securely anchor water heaters, and all other types of gas heaters and furnaces to the floor and/or wall. The water heater should be bolted to the floor and anchored to the wall with a single metal strap bolted to the studs of the wall on each side about half way up the water heater.

- Keep a cresent wrench near or attached to your gas meter and know how to shut the gas off. See Section UTILITIES.

FURNITURE

- Place stereos and other heavy radio equipment on low stable cabinets, or on the lower shelves, to prevent them from falling.

- Arrange your furniture in such a manner that there are clear accessible escape routes in every room.

- Modular bookcases and shelves made with bricks and boards are especially dangerous because the pieces are of varying weights and are not interlocked or connected. They should be well braced or avoided altogether.

- When hanging pictures and mirrors, use closed eye bolts on each side of the hanging object and one screwed into a wall stud. Run picture wire through all three eye bolts beginning with the one at the end of the picture (A), next through the bolt on the wall (B), and then through the other end (C). (See illustration)

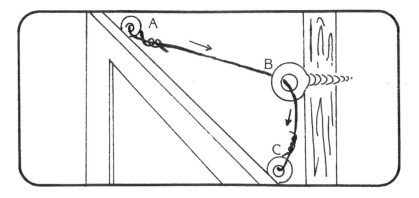

- Do not hang heavy pictures or mirrors over beds or have anything near beds that could fall and injure anyone while sleeping.

- High bookcases and tall furniture should be securely anchored to the studs in the walls. Brackets or the method used for hanging pictures and mirrors would also work well for this.

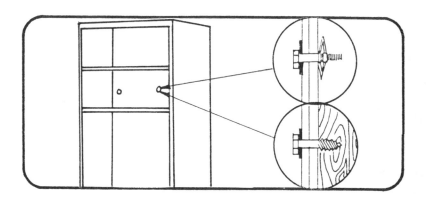

- Place beds in a position away from windows.

 Furniture that people will use, such as chairs, couches, beds, should not be placed near objects that can fall and cause injury.

- The safest place for a TV or radio antenna is to anchor it to the side of the house. If it must be installed on the roof, put it in the middle and anchor it securely with cables. Never put the antenna near the chimney or edge of the roof.

- If you work or live above the third floor of a building, all heavy pieces of furniture, such as tables and desks, should be bolted to the floor or securely anchored to the walls. The vibrations from the ground tend to be accentuated and increase when they reach the upper stories of a building.

HOUSEHOLD ITEMS

- Make sure light fixtures, hanging plants, clocks, etc., are securely anchored to studs in the walls or ceilings.

- Place large or heavy objects on the lower shelves, but do not mix heavy and light items. The lighter ones could be crushed by the heavier ones when the shaking starts.

- Some kind of railing should be installed on open shelves to prevent their contents from falling. This can be done attractively with doweling or decorative edging.

- Install clips, latches or other locking devices on all cupboards and cabinets. This will stop the doors from popping open and dumping the contents which can cause injuries as well as damage. This is especially important in the kitchen.

- The best way to protect fine china, crystal, and other expensive glassware is to store it in cupboards on racks designed to hold the pieces separately, or in drawers.

SAFETY

- All windows that extend to the floor should be provided with strong guard rails on every floor above the first story.

- Check your yard and nearby area for the safest place away from power lines, chimneys, fences that may fall, etc., and use it for your family's safe area to get together after an earthquake or any other disaster. Make sure all family members know where the safe area is and that they are to go there after the shaking stops.

- Hold occasional home earthquake drills · get your family familiar with and used to taking the correct action automatically. This will help minimize injury and avoid panic in your family during an earthquake.

- Anytime you enter a building you are not familiar with, locate and make a mental note of all exits. This is important for other disasters as well as earthquakes.

HAZARDOUS STORAGE

- Store houshold chemicals and cleaners in airtight (non-breakable) plastic containers in a low, LOCKED cabinet where children cannot get at them. Follow manufacturers instructions and cautions.

    ✓ *What dangerous substances do you have on hand?*
    ✓ *Do you really need them?*
    ✓ *How often are they used?*

    Discard any that are unnecessary. Make sure chemicals cannot become mixed under any conditions.

- Carefully store flammable, poisonous, and volatile liquids such as paints, thinners, and pesticides in unbreakable containers in low, LOCKED cabinets outside your living area.

DURING AN EARTHQUAKE

Since most injuries are caused by falling debris, always be aware of your surroundings and the potential danger you are in from falling objects.

The first and most important thing to remember:
REMAIN CALM. You will be taken by surprise in an earthquake, there is no earthquake watch or warning. You may only have a second in which to save your life. Decide where the safest place is and go there.

INSIDE

- If you are indoors, STAY INDOORS. Watch out for high bookcases, china cabinets, shelves and other furniture which might slide or fall over. Stay away from all windows.

- If you're home, take cover in the strongest area near you. Go to your preselected area (see Section HOME DISASTER PLAN) if you have time, otherwise get in a hallway or under a doorframe, against an inside wall, under a table (sturdy), bed, in a closet. Put something solid and strong between you and flying glass, parts of the ceiling or other falling debris.

- Cover your face with your arms if threatened with falling debris.

- Stay away from chimneys.

Highrise buildings

Get under a desk or similar piece of furniture or stand under a doorway or against an inside wall away from windows. Do not run for exits since stairways may be broken and jammed with people. Do not use elevators.

Crowded store

DO NOT RUSH FOR EXITS — hundreds of people will have the same idea. People in crowds tend to panic easy and more are killed by trampling than any other way.

If you have to leave, choose an exit as carefully as possible. BUT, DON'T PANIC. **IF YOU ARE ALREADY IN A SAFE AREA - STAY THERE.**

OUTSIDE

- If you are outside, STAY OUTSIDE. Move away from buildings and areas that may have falling glass, electrical wires, poles and debris.

- If you are in a moving car, stop as quickly and safely as possible and stay inside the vehicle. When you drive on, watch for hazards such as fallen wires and roads that could be undermined (supporting materials moved or washed away from under road) from ground movement or water from broken pipes.

- Do not stop your vehicle on or under bridges, overpasses, trees, street lights, power poles, or signs. Try to move your car as far as possible out of the normal traffic pattern.

- In hilly or mountainous terrain watch out for falling rocks or other debris that could be loosened by the earthquake. You can expect danger from one rock or a landslide.

- Be prepared for aftershocks. Although most of these are smaller than the main tremor, some could be large enough to cause more damage. And, the first tremor may not be the main shock, the big one could still be coming.

AFTER AN EARTHQUAKE

- Remain calm. Stop a minute and think! (*This is your most important minute.*)

 Think what your emergency plan calls for — THEN DO IT.

Don't change your plans without a good reason. Your plans were made while you were calm and thinking rationally.

- Check for injuries to yourself, your family, your neighbors. Do not attempt to move seriously injured persons unless they are in immediate danger of further injury.

- If you are trapped under debris, do your best to stay calm-don't make any sudden moves. Signal for help by banging on pipes or something that will make enough noise for rescue workers to hear you. Reserve your energy because it may take some time before help arrives. Do not do anything to make things worse.

- Check utility lines and appliances for damage. If gas leaks exist, shut off main gas valve. Shut off electricity if there is any damage to the house wiring. Report damage to the appropriate utility companies and follow their instructions.

- If you smell gas, or gas leaks are suspected, DO NOT operate electrical switches, appliances, or your phone. This may cause sparks that can ignite gas or other flammable fumes.

- Use flashlight for lighting if you have one · Do not use candles ·· DO NOT LIGHT MATCHES OR USE OTHER OPEN FLAMES either during or after an earthquake.

- Do not use your telephone except for genuine emergency calls: only medical, fire and violent crime emergencies qualify. Turn on your portable radio or TV to an emergency station/channel for information and instructions.

- If there has been major damage to your area, turn your water main off until you are sure the incoming water lines are intact and the water is not contaminated. This way you will save the water already in your pipes for drinking and cooking.

- Make sure that sewer lines are intact before allowing the toilets to be flushed.

- Do not touch downed power lines or objects touched by the downed wires.

- Check your chimney over its entire length for cracks and damage, particularly at the attic and at the roof line. Look for separations where the chimney and fireplace are connected to the adjacent walls, ceilings and roof, inside and out. Unnoticed damage could lead to fire. The initial check should be made from a distance. Approach chimneys with caution.

- Thoroughly check your home or building for structural damage. Look for cracks, sags and other irregularities in the ceilings, walls and floors. If you have any doubts about the safety of your home stay out of it until it can be checked by a professional building inspector.

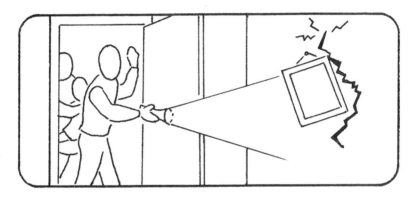

- Check to make sure built-in cupboards and light fixtures remain properly connected to the walls and ceilings. They might have been weakened by the initial shock and aftershocks could bring them crashing down on top of you.

- Stay tuned to local radio and TV for instructions on where to go for medical attention, necessary emergency assistance for housing, clothing and food.

  Ways to help yourself and your community recover from the emergency will also be announced and many volunteers will be needed.

- Immediately clean up spilled medicines, drugs, and other potentially harmful materials.

- DO NOT eat or drink anything from an open container that is near broken glass such as windows or dishes.

- Be careful when you check closets and cupboards. Open doors slowly and watch out for objects falling from the shelves.

- If your house is unsafe to occupy, you must find some type of shelter, particularly if weather conditions are unfavorable. You should have the choice of a public shelter. However, if the damage to your community is of major proportions, you may not have this option. Your only alternative might be to improvise shelter in a safe section of your yard or some other clear area. See Section SHELTERS.

- Stay away from beaches and other waterfront areas. There could be a real danger of tsunamis (tidal waves).

- Pay special attention to your children's needs, emotional as well as physical. Be truthful but reassuring when answering their questions and encourage them to talk about their experience to relieve anxieties. Maintain a positive attitude - for your own sake as well as theirs.

- During clean-up, keep an accurate record of everything that was damaged or destroyed and try to document this with pictures. Save pieces of valuable items to back up your insurance claims.

- Do not go sightseeing. Keep streets clear for emergency vehicles. If you must travel, drive carefully along debris-filled streets. Roads may be undermined and can collapse from the weight of your car.

- Take extra precautions to prevent fires. Lowered water pressure caused by broken pipes will make fire fighting difficult.

- Assist police, fire fighting, civil defense personnel when your help is requested. Cooperate fully when asked, but keep out of the way of disaster-emergency operations.

SITE SELECTION FOR YOUR HOME

There are many factors that can influence the amount of shaking and damage any piece of property will sustain during an earthquake. The most important are:

- ✓ Proximity to fault
- ✓ Geologic foundation
- ✓ Landforms
- ✓ Surrounding terrain
- ✓ Construction materials
- ✓ Construction design
- ✓ Workmanship
- ✓ Foundation

If you are planning to build or buy a home in an area where earthquakes are prevalent, there are a number of factors you should know about in selecting a site and particular type of construction.

Before you purchase a home or piece of property on which to build a home, you should first obtain a geologic map of the area showing all active and inactive faults. The map is very important because a fault is not always visible and any visible signs could also have been masked by the developers. If the piece of property in question is within an active fault zone, beware of the implications before you buy it. Even if the property is in an inactive fault zone, think about hiring a geologist to investigate the area and go by his recommendations. Remember, buying property is a big investment and when you are buying in earthquake prone areas you are taking a risk.

If you are already buying a home that is in an active fault zone, it may also be wise to hire a geologist to find out if the fault has had displacements or creep in the past and what to do about it.

Another important factor to check on is the geologic foundation. Watch out for:

- Areas where there is a thick layer of soft soil or a mixture of soft soil and broken up bedrock. These landforms change small shock waves in the bedrock beneath them into larger, more slow moving, more intense shock waves at the surface. Also, avoid building sites on deep loose soil at the base of a hill because shock waves coming from deep soil strike up against the solid bedrock of a hill and bounce back causing more damage.

- Avoid landfills over old lake beds, riversides, dumpsites, swamps and other similar areas. These present a problem with liquifaction. This occurs when the vibrations from an earthquake cause the soil particles to settle and the water in the soil to rise creating a soil that resembles quicksand. Liquifaction occurs most frequently near large inland bodies of water and ocean front properties.

- Areas prone to landslides are another problem and should be avoided when possible. Be aware of the fact that some landslides are not the result of natural forces but have been set up by improper grading and filling of construction sites on hillsides.

Other factors to consider when purchasing a home are its proximity to other buildings that may fall on it in an earthquake, and its proximity to other hazards such as water tanks, oil refineries and high voltage power lines.

You should give some serious thought to the risks before buying a home or property below a dam or near a dike or levee.

You will save yourself both money and trouble by thoroughly investigating any property you wish to purchase.

STRUCTURAL SAFETY

Make sure your house is securely attached to its foundation with anchor bolts or by some equivalent means. If you are buying or already own an older building, there is a chance it is not anchored to the foundation. If this is the case, it is imperative that you take corrective action because the shock waves from an earthquake can easily knock the entire structure off its foundation

The buildings that will suffer the most damage in an earthquake are those made of unreinforced brick. The walls are subject to collapse because there is little flexibility and the mortar separates easily. There are ways to strengthen such structures but it can be very costly and you should consult an engineer who specializes in earthquake reinforcement.

If you are buying or own a home built out of concrete blocks you should ensure it has been properly constructed with steel reinforcement bars and the cavities completely filled with concrete.

Wooden structures are generally the safest as far as surviving a large earthquake because of the flexible nature of the wood. However, these buildings must be properly designed and constructed. The workmanship and quality of materials are also very important factors to consider.

Air conditioners and water tanks should never be placed on the roof. The added weight could make the roof collapse when ordinarily it might withstand the shaking.

FIRES

FIRE

Every fire needs three elements to burn: fuel, heat and oxygen. A fire is the result of enough heat being applied to the fuel. In simple terms, fire is a rapid chemical combination of fuel, heat, and oxygen. Once the fire has started it gives itself its own life producing heat. To extinguish a fire you must remove one or more of these three elements.

Fire authorities agree that the great majority of people caught in fires could escape if they knew even only a few facts about fire and its killing power or if they had planned ahead what they would do if fire struck. You don't have to know very much, you don't need to make elaborate plans. But you owe it to yourself and your family to take a few minutes to plan what precautions to take, what to do and how to save yourselves if your house or apartment burns.

THE DANGER OF FIRE

Smoke, not flames, is the real killer in a fire. In fact, very few persons burn to death. The fumes and smoke are far more deadly than the flames. As many as 80% of the fire-related victims were asphyxiated by toxic fumes long before flames ever touched them.

Wherever there is smoke, there is potential danger-so get out, and get out fast. Smoke being hot always rises. This is important if you live and/or work in a two or more story house or building.

Fire is most likely to attack you when you are least likely to be aware of danger — at night when you are sleeping. You can't count on the smell of smoke to wake you, but even if it does you may have already inhaled so much of it that you can only get a few feet or to your hallway before passing out. Your bedroom door is the most effective barrier against the fire. That slab of wood, any fireman will tell you, is a lifesaving wall between yourself and fire, but only if it is a CLOSED BARRIER. Open, your door won't stop the flames or smoke. Recent tests show that an ordinary bedroom door will hold back heat and lethal gases for a few minutes (5 to 10 minutes only) giving you a little time to escape.

Your family should get into the habit of closing their bedroom doors at night. Follow through by reminding them as often as necessary until they do it automatically. If you're concerned about not being able to hear small children behind a closed door, check into an inexpensive intercom.

Too often, however, someone smelling smoke will fling open the door, and they are overcome by a blast of hot air and fumes, and the loss of oxygen in the burning area. If you suspect fire, NEVER open a bedroom door without first checking to see if there is heat. Place a hand on the panel at the top of the door; if it is even slightly warm, DON'T OPEN THAT DOOR. Wood is a very poor conducter of heat, so when the wood feels hot it means that very high temperatures and smoke are on the other side, and will burst in on you. If possible, escape out a bedroom window. If not, stuff a small rug, towel, sheet or other fabric around the cracks of the door to keep out smoke, and wait to be rescued.

There are three signs of fire, flames, heat and smoke. If any one of these is present, GET OUT OF THE BUILDING. If there is more than one floor, use the stairs only. DO NOT use the elevators.

BE AWARE THAT:

- Children too often don't try to escape at all. They lock themselves in closets or hide under beds and rugs, waiting for someone to rescue them.

- Many adults have refused to follow firemen to safety and have had to be dragged out bodily.

- Other fire victims don't try to get out because they don't know the killing power and speed of fire, believing they have plenty of time to escape.

- Many lose their lives because they try to rescue possessions instead of getting themselves out, or even go back into the burning building for some thing. Nothing is worth the loss of a life — GET OUT OF THE BUILDING.

- You should call the Fire Department from another place, a neighbor's, etc., if there is any risk to you or another family member.

- Some consider a small fire not important enough to "bother" alerting other members of the family or the Fire Department. This can and is tragic. No matter how small and insignificant a fire seems, evacuate everyone immediately.

Life is much harder to replace than property, and in a fire you can rarely save both.

WHEN REPORTING A FIRE

STAY CALM — If you get rattled and mess up giving the information you will have to repeat it and that wastes time. Think what you're going to tell them and give the necessary information as follows:

1. The family name
    Address - number, street name, (if apartment give building and apartment number) and
    City. Also the nearest cross streets
    Repeat the information if asked.

2. Tell what happened - where or what area of your home is on fire, i.e., the furnace exploded, a grass fire is coming toward your house, oil or gasoline fire in garage.

    When you have finished, don't hang up. Wait to see if your information was understood or if more information is needed.

IN ANY FIRE THE NO. 1 PRIORITY IS SAVING LIVES

AT HOME:

Get everyone out of the building or danger area safely.

Section FAMILY HOME DISASTER PLAN tells you how to make an emergency escape route plan for your home. If trapped upstairs, use rope or ladder to get out window, or tie sheets or clothing together and anchor onto something strong enough to hold it.

CALL THE FIRE DEPARTMENT from a neighboring phone or alarm box. The fire department should be notified no matter how small the fire is.

DO NOT GO BACK INTO A BURNING BUILDING. Make one member of your family responsible for everyone staying in the "safe" area. Do not allow anyone to go back into the fire to retrieve any possession. It can be a very deadly "dumb thing" to risk your life for something or some possession.

Have someone in a safe area that can give information to the Fire Department as they arrive.

AT WORK OR IN A BUILDING SOMEWHERE

Get yourself and your companions out of the building or danger area safely. REMEMBER: Fire, smoke and heat all rise, stay low and close to the floor and cover your face with a wet cloth if possible

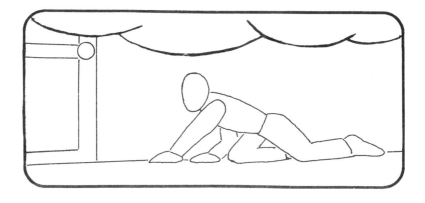

If the fire is in a large building with elevators · DO NOT USE THE ELEVATORS, only use the stairway for safety.

CALL THE FIRE DEPARTMENT · Set off the fire alarm. and follow up with a phone call, if you can from another building.

Your company should have an evacuation plan for your building, find out what it is and who is in charge of their disaster plan program. If they do not have one, why don't you suggest that a proper plan be made.

All buildings and places of business must have a fire alarm system, learn ahead of time where it is and how to operate it.

Do NOT go back into a burning building. Try to stop anyone else from entering the building also—those papers cannot be that important.

FIGHTING FIRE

There are different types of fires—chemical, grease, electrical, upholstery, structural, and others, and different ways of handling each one with safety. A small fire can be put out while it is still small if you stay calm and act quickly.

REMEMBER—every fire needs three things to burn: Fuel, Heat and Oxygen. To extinguish a fire you must remove one or more of these.

 The fire department should be notified no matter how small the fire is.

GREASE FIRE—

Cover, smother, and extinguish. If a pan catches fire while cooking, IMMEDIATELY:

- Turn the burner off.

- Use the lid as a shield and cover the pan with it.

 NEVER use water on a fire involving grease, oil, gasoline or other flammable liquids.

- Or smother with baking soda by sprinkling evenly and thickly over entire pan. Do not dump a big glob in one spot as the grease will overflow out the other side and spread the fire or burn off. Sprinkle it in carefully. DO NOT use flour, cornstarch or other vegetable products. They will burn and add more fuel to the fire.

- Or, use the recommended fire extinguisher (see below)

- Call the fire department.

- Do NOT attempt to carry a flaming pan to the sink or carry through a room to take outdoors.

ELECTRICAL FIRE

- If possible, unplug appliance or cord.

- Shut off electricity at main switch box.

- Get everyone out of the danger area.

- Have someone call the Fire Department.

- Use a dry chemical (powder) extinguisher to put out fire, or water ONLY IF CURRENT IS OFF. NEVER use water on a fire where current is still on.

 If a gas leak is suspected, do not use telephone in the vicinity of the leak. Telephones contain electrical contacts, and when you lift the hand set and dial it can generate a tiny spark that could set off an explosion if the gas content is high enough.

- If a live wire is down outside — DO NOT TOUCH OR GET NEAR IT or any wet area that may be touching it. Do not let anyone else touch it.

- Call the police and electric company

UPHOLSTERY FIRE — Couch, overstuffed chair, sofa, mattress, or any piece of furniture with padding.

- If in flames, and confined to single piece of furniture, evacuate everyone, then spray with fire extinguisher and call Fire Department.

- If smoldering, evacuate everyone
   - Have someone call fire department,
   - Use extinguisher or pour water on smoldering area,
   - With help move piece of furniture to outside area.

- Make sure the fire department checks the furniture to be sure the fire is out. The padding can smolder for hours and reignite when no one is around.

PERSONAL CLOTHING FIRE

If you or someone near you should have their clothing catch on fire, **DO NOT RUN — NEVER RUN**

- **STOP, COVER YOU FACE, DROP AND ROLL ON THE GROUND.** Continue rolling over slowly until the flames are out.

- Smother the flames with blanket, coat, shirt, anything handy that will put the flames out as fast as possible without catching fire too.

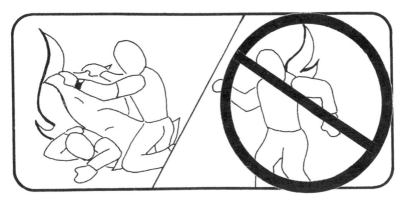

- Never try to remove clothing or pieces of charred material.

- Douse with cool water. Cover burned areas with soaking wet sterile dressings, or freshly washed sheets, pillowcases, linens, *but nothing with starch*. In cases of extreme burns where clothing is still smoking and very hot, pouring water (cool) over the victim can help cool the burned area. Keep victim calm.

- Call the Fire Department and Paramedics immediately.

FIRE PREVENTION

ELECTRICAL

- Check electrical wiring throughout home, other cords and appliances. Replace all worn or frayed cords. Do not run cords under carpets.

- Use irons and other heating appliances with care. Irons unattended can, if the thermostat fails, become so hot they will become a glob of molten metal and burn whatever they are resting on.

- Use safety plug covers in all sockets not in use, especially those low enough for children to reach and stick wires and other things into.

- Do not dry stuffed toys, pillows, or padded bras containing foam rubber in your dryer. They can dry quickly and heat to their flash point causing a fire in the dryer.

- Do not overload wall sockets or extension plugs with appliances.

- Keep enough space behind your TV set to keep air ventilation circulating. Overheating causes fires.

- Turn off switches or unplug before changing bulbs or fixing christmas lights.

- APPLIANCES—Each appliance must have its own proper plug and ground, if in doubt, check the manufacturer's instruction manual.

POWER TOOLS

- Keep in good working order, protect them and their cords from damage, store safely in dry place.

- Don't use near any type of flammable gases.

- When using out of doors keep cords out of water, never use in rain, on wet surfaces, or grass/ground.

FIREPLACE

- Always use a screen on a fireplace to prevent sparks from popping into the room and igniting carpet, etc.

- Never burn trash and papers in the fireplace, as the ashes could ignite a roof, yours or your neighbors.

- Clean chimney and flue at least once a year.

- Do NOT burn christmas tree in fireplace – the branches contain sap that will ignite and burn fast and can get out of control.

- Never leave any fire unattended in your fireplace.

FIREWORKS

- Do not take fireworks apart.

- Never make or use homemade fireworks or illegal fireworks. They are responsible for burning, injuring, and killing many people every year. Use approved / safe / sane fireworks only.

- Never throw lighted fireworks. They can burn people, clothing, homes, grass, etc.

- Dispose of fireworks by dropping in bucket or large can of water.

FURNACE

- Check your furnace annually, prior to cold season, for plugged up or worn outlets, weak pilot light, nonworking controls. In most areas the gas company will come out and check and/or fix for you.

SMOKING

- Never smoke in bed

- Never smoke near flammable liquids or materials.

- Never empty ash trays into trash containers, especially at night. Leave ashtrays sitting out until morning to ensure all cigarettes are completely out.

- Always make sure cigarettes, cigars, and pipes are completely out before leaving unattended in room or car.

- Always use a proper ashtray for cigarettes, cigars and pipes.

- Do not set burning cigarette on the edge of counter, sink, furniture, or anything that it can fall out of or off. They will leave burn marks on wood furniture that are permanent, and if they drop onto the floor or carpet can start a fire.

BARBEQUE - HIBATCHIS

- Never use a barbeque or hibatchi indoors or in a vehicle. The fire will produce carbon monoxide fumes which is deadly.

- Never add any fire starter to charcoals or other fire if heat or flames are present.

- Charcoals on the market made with the lighter fluid already on them may become a potential fire hazard. If they get wet and then warmed up, for example by the sun, they may ignite. If you use these, store with safety in cool, dry area.

GENERAL SAFETY TIPS

- Never leave any fire unattended · barbeque, fireplace, campfire.

- Handle or use flammable liquids in the open or in well ventilated areas only, away from any source that would ignite it.

- Never leave candles or any open flame burning in a room unattended.

- Keep matches, lighters, and other combustibles stored in high places, away from small children.

- Use gasoline and other explosive substances with extreme caution and in well ventilated area only. It only takes a minute spark to ignite fumes and/or vapors from these.

- Make sure your christmas tree has water to keep it green. Always use a stand that will hold water.

- Do not let trash or junk accumulate in small areas. Clean out attics, closets and garages often.

- If there are trees around your home, keep pruned of dead branches and cut them back so they do not touch the buildings.

- If you live in an area with thick or heavy vegetation, clear the brush from around your home, garage, and any other buildings. A safe area would be at least 30 feet.

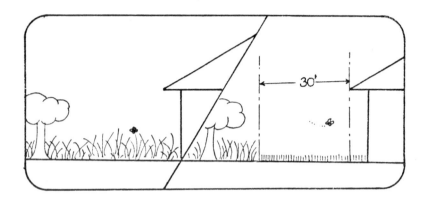

- Check with your local fire department for any requirements and suggestions for clearing your home of any fire hazards.

TOOLS FOR FIRE SAFETY

SMOKE DETECTORS

No matter what type of dwelling you live in, smoke detectors are very important and should be standard equipment for your home.

- The number of smoke detectors you need depends upon the layout of your home. Smoke detectors should be placed in the hallway on the ceiling or the wall near the ceiling outside bedroom doors. If all of the bedrooms or sleeping areas are located at one end of the house, one smoke alarm should be sufficient.

- If there are bedrooms in two or more sections of the house, it is essential to have smoke detectors in each area where a person sleeps.

- If your home has more than one floor, you need to have at least one smoke detector on each floor.

LADDERS

- If you live in a multi-storied house or apartment and there are bedrooms or areas where people sleep above the first floor, it is vital that you keep a rope ladder or equivalent means of escape in each and every bedroom, preferably under the bed and easily accessible. This can be a matter of life and death for everyone who sleeps upstairs.

HOSES

- You should keep a garden hose long enough to reach any room on that floor in each story of your home. It should be stored under the bathroom sink with any connections that are needed.

FIRE EXTINGUISHERS

Remember, fire extinguishers are designed to put out small fires, not big ones.

They are labeled A, B, or C, according to the type of fire they are to be used on. Using one type of extinguisher on a different type of fire can make that fire worse. There are also multi-purpose extinguishers, labeled ABC, that can be used to put out most types of fires.

Ordinary Combustibles

Label A — water-type
Paper, cloth, wood, rubber, and many plastics

Flammable Liquids

Label B
Oils, gasoline, some paints, lacquers, solvents and other flammable liquids, grease from frying pan or oven

Electrical Equipment

Label C
Wiring, fuse boxes, energized electrical equipment, other electrical sources

FIRST AID FOR MINOR BURNS

If you have been trained in First Aid you will know what to do until help arrives. Many excellent courses are taught to prepare people for emergencies such as this. An extra benefit from this type of training is that you can use it to take care of small emergencies on an everyday basis. For more information on First Aid classes contact your local Red Cross.

HOT GREASE AND OTHER THERMAL BURNS: Immediately submerge burned area in cool water. Call paramedics or get medical attention as necessary.

CHEMICAL BURNS — POWDERED: First remove clothing and brush off as much as possible, then flush with copious amounts of water, with hose or shower if handy, for at least 5 minutes. Get medical attention.

ELECTRICAL BURNS: Cover with clean, DRY, sterile dressing. Get medical attention.

Never put grease or oil of any type on any type of burn. Immerse it in or pour cool or cold water on the affected area. The burned area is still hot, adding oil/grease will heat that oil/grease and it will continue burning the affected area. The most important thing to remember is "cool the burned area down," but don't use ice.

FLOODS

FLOODS

A flood is a deluge of water covering an otherwise normally dry land area often with little or no prior warning.

Floods are caused by: excessive rainfall; cloud bursts; rivers flooding; rapid snow melt; dams or levees overflowing or breaking; hurricanes; tsunamis/tidal waves. With heavy rainfall they can occur in areas with some vegetation, as well as barren or burned land.

A flood's initial damage can be as severe as a tornado, but the devastation in its aftermath can be much worse. Flooding can do as little as flood an intersection or totally destroy your home and neighborhood.

Aside from the destruction of water, mud and debris, floods bring a high potential for health hazards by spreading diseases such as typhoid, diptheria, cholera, hepatitis and others. These diseases are brought on by bodies of animals and other debris decaying and contaminating the water, or mosquitos and bacteria breeding in stagnant water.

MAJOR CAUSES OF FLOODING

- *HEAVY RAINFALL*

    Heavy rainfall has to go somewhere. If it falls on hilly terrain, it will naturally run downhill and follow the lowest paths. It can cause small creeks, streambeds, gullies, ravines, roads following the base of the hills, culverts, or any low-lying ground to flood rapidly, usually before any warning can be given. The steeper the sides of the water-flow area, the faster and more destructive the water will be. Whether camping, visiting or living near a river or stream, or an area with mountains or hills nearby, you should always be aware of the potential for flooding and the necessary steps to safety.

- ***STREAMS/RIVERS OVERFLOWING***

  Streams and rivers overflow their banks because of heavy rainfall, fast snow melt, etc. The danger is not only in the immediate area of the rainfall. Rain does not have to be directly overhead to cause flood waters. A storm in the mountains or hills upstream from you will wash water into your area flooding it.

- ***DAM BREAKING***

  If you live in an area below or downstream from a dam, learn all the warning signals for your area and the safe areas nearby for evacuation. Most likely there will be very little time to get to safety. The warning sirens (or other alarms) may be your only warning of the approaching danger. HEED THEM, PLAN AHEAD and PREPARE FOR IT.

FLASH FLOODS

Flash floods are primarily caused by heavy rainfall in foothills or mountainous terrain. The water comes down so fast it doesn't have time to soak in, causing most of it to run off. This heavy run-off collects and flows rapidly out of the lowest opening from the hills and onto any flat area. Rushing water pours onto the lowest level of ground seeking its own level, which means it will cover as wide an area as it needs, usually sweeping anything in its path with it. This can include buildings, vehicles, trees, mud, rocks, and other debris. The depth of water can be very shallow when it spreads across the flat area; but, because of the force of its momentum, it can be deadly.

Whether camping, visiting, or living near a river or stream or an area with mountains or hills nearby, you should always be aware of the potential for flooding and the necessary steps to safety.

There are two types of flashflood advisories issued by the National Weather Service:

- *Flash Flood WATCH:*

    Heavy rains occurring or expected to occur may cause flash flooding in certain areas and people should be alert to the possibility of a flood emergency that will require immediate action.

- *Flash Flood WARNING:*

    Flash floods are occurring or are imminent on certain streams or designated areas and immediate action should be taken by those threatened.

Always be aware of the hazards and possibilities of flash floods during any period of heavy rainfall and be prepared to take evasive action immediately. If you see any signs of flooding, move to safer ground immediately. If possible, notify local authorities of the danger so others can be warned.

ON THE ROAD

If you are traveling during periods of heavy rainfall, take the following precautions:

- ALWAYS REMAIN CALM — panic kills.

- STAY AWAY FROM NATURAL STREAMBEDS and other drainage channels both during and after rainstorms.

- KNOW WHERE YOU ARE AT ALL TIMES. Use your maps to tell you where there is low ground. You don't have to be at the bottom of a hill to be in the path of dangerous flash flood waters.

- KNOW WHERE THERE IS HIGH GROUND and how to get there in a hurry. In many cases roads and trails run parallel to existing drainage channels and can be swept away by flood waters.

- STAY OUT OF FLOODED AREAS. The water may still be rising and currents are usually swift.

 As in any kind of flood, never attempt to cross a flowing stream on foot if the water goes above your knees.

- ABANDON STALLED VEHICLES IN FLOODED AREAS if you can do so safely. Vehicles can easily be swept away by rising flood waters. DO NOT attempt to move stalled vehicles. Get out and move to higher ground. *Take the easiest, safest route out of the water.*

FLOODING IN POPULATED AREAS

Cities and towns are often subject to flooding due to heavy rainfall and inadequate drainage systems. Most often this means that streets, mostly corners with low curbs, are flooded and driving through them can be hazardous. However, in many towns and cities there is a real problem of flooding where homes and neighborhoods can be flooded and evacuation necessary.

In many instances, underpasses and low areas of main roads, freeways, turnpikes, etc., become flooded. This is especially dangerous because of the depth of the water—it can not only stall your vehicle but also submerge it.

Always be aware of all street, safety, or other warning signs and signals especially those that are temporarily placed to warn you of hazards, real and potential. Pay attention to them—they are put there for YOUR safety.

PLANNING AHEAD

- Find the elevation of your property in relation to any possible flood levels for your area. It may help you to know the effects on your home of predicted flood levels that are broadcast.

- If you live in an area where you might be subjected to a flood at any time, it would be wise to carry flood insurance. If your community has adopted flood plain management measures, you will be eligible to apply for the National Flood Insurance Program. For more information contact: The Federal Emergency Management Agency, Federal Insurance Administration, Washington, D.C. 20472.

- Learn the safest routes from your home or work place to high, safe ground should a flood occur and practice taking these routes so you will be prepared when you only have minutes to get to safety.

- Plan a method of getting to your roof in case you become stranded and unable to evacuate before high flood waters occur.

- Stock extra fuel, water, and ready-to-eat foods. Follow the same guidelines for stocking emergency supplies as you would for any other disaster, but store it high if you live in a flood-prone area. Also, put it where it's easily accessible and can be moved in a hurry without difficulty. Don't forget about supplies for your pets.

- Keep waterproofing materials on hand such as plastic sheeting, sandbags, plywood and other lumber.

- Keep automobile filled with gas.

- Have battery-operated flashlights and radio, with extra batteries and bulbs, and candles and waterproof matches handy and easily accessible.

If your home is not in danger, you will probably be better off staying put. The agencies in charge will warn you to evacuate your home because of impending flood dangers if and when it becomes necessary.

IF A FLOOD IS THREATENING

If you have time, there are a few things you should do before leaving, BUT ONLY IF TIME PERMITS.

- Open basement windows to equalize water pressure on the foundation and walls.

- If you are going to be flooded DO NOT stack sandbags around the outside walls of your house to keep the water out of your basement. Water can seep down anyway and the pressure it puts on the walls and under the floor can cause structural damage. It is usually better to let the flood water flow freely into the basement or flood it yourself to equalize the pressure caused by the water outside, thereby avoiding damage to the foundation and the house.

- Shut off your utilities before leaving your home if you have time.

- Unplug all electrical appliances that cannot be moved. BUT NEVER touch them if you are standing in water, wet flooring, or you are wet.

- Secure all movable objects such as lawn furniture, garbage cans, garden tools, etc. that could be washed or blown away. Move them inside or tie them down.

- Move essential items and furniture to upper floors or as high as possible.

- Lock all doors and windows to your house. Park any car you are not using in your garage and roll up all windows and lock the doors.

DURING A FLOOD

- Do not use your telephone except for genuine emergency calls. Listen to you radio for instructions.

- Stay tuned to your local radio for instructions on what to do until help arrives, how to get medical attention, necessary emergency assistance for housing, clothing, and food, and ways to help yourself and your community recover from the flood.

- Remain in a safe area until informed by local authorities that it is safe to leave.

- Never let your children play around canals or any moving water.

- Respond to requests for help from police, fire fighting, civil defense, and relief organizations; but do not go into damaged areas unless your help has been requested. Always cooperate with public safety officials.

- When helping someone in moving water, for your own safety throw a preserver or hold a rope, stick, or something else out to them, instead of jumping into the water yourself.

IF YOU ARE BEING EVACUATED

In some locations, your local government will be able to arrange transportation for you. If this is the case, precautions will be taken for your safety. If you are walking or driving your own car, keep in mind the following:

 Always follow the instructions and advice of the authorities in your area. If they tell you to evacuate, do so as quickly as possible.

- If you are sent to a particular location, DON'T GO ANYWHERE ELSE. And don't take short cuts. Use the travel routes specified or recommended by the authorities. They have the most up-to-date information and, therefore, are able to plan the safest routes and procedures to expedite your evacuation with the least amount of danger.

- Always TRAVEL WITH EXTREME CAUTION.

- Listen to the radio for locations of emergency shelters and assistance.

- Leave early enough to avoid being trapped by flooded roads.

- Avoid areas where rivers or streams may flood suddenly.

- Be on the alert for washed out or undermined roads, slides, downed utility wires, broken water mains, and falling objects and other obstructions in the road.

- Never attempt to cross a flooded area or stream unless you are sure the water will not be above your knees or the middle of the wheels on your car. If it is safe to drive across, proceed very slowly, with your car in low gear, to avoid splashing water into the engine and causing it to stall.

 If your vehicle stalls while crossing any type of moving water, GET OUT IMMEDIATELY AND MOVE TO HIGH GROUND. Take the shortest and safest route out of the water.

- Always test your brakes after going through deep water.

If you are trapped inside your house and unable to evacuate because of high water:

- Get out of your house and onto the roof before high water seals off all escape routes, like the windows.

- If forced to the roof of your house, spread something large, such as a sheet, shirt, or jacket, over one area to show that someone is on the roof and needs rescuing. Make a big 'X' or arrow if you have enough materials.

- TO SIGNAL: Put a sign in the window 'SEND HELP'. Think in 3's, the standard call for help: three horn blasts, pause, three more; flash your lights 3 times, pause, flash 3 times again. Repeat in three's.

- If you need to be evacuated by boat or helicopter, be ready to go when assistance arrives.

 If you are being evacuated or rescued by boat, **DO NOT JUMP IN.** Wait for instructions from the rescue personnel in the boat. You can swamp the boat and put more people in danger.

 If you are being rescued by a helicopter, **WAIT FOR INSTRUCTIONS. When a line or rope is lowered to you, NEVER, NEVER tie, anchor, or attach it to anything with the idea of holding it at your location.** Helicopters operate under extremely hazardous conditions, especially when doing rescue work near the ground. You could cause it to crash.

AFTER THE FLOOD

- Do not go sightseeing if travel is possible. The disaster agencies will need clear roads to handle emergencies.

- If you must travel, drive carefully along debris-filled streets. Roads may be undermined and can collapse from the weight of the car.

- DO NOT eat or drink anything that has come in contact with flood water.

- Test drinking water for potability. Ground wells should be pumped out and tested before drinking.

- Check with your local agency for information regarding the suitability and advisability of using tap water. See Section WATER on ways to purify water.

- Use the same precautions that you would follow after an earthquake.

- If your home or business has been damaged by the flood, call your insurance broker or agent immediately.

- On returning to your home, be sure the structure is not in danger of collapsing before you enter the house.

- Open doors and windows and let the air circulate to clear out foul odors and protect you from escaping gas. Don't use matches or open flame when you enter the house.

CLEAN-UP

- Watch out for live electrical wires. Make sure the electricity is turned off at the main source. Do not use any lights or appliances until an electrician has checked your system.

- Begin cleaning up as soon as possible. Discard any perishable foods that could have been contaminated.

- Immediately clean up spilled medicines, drugs, and other potentially harmful materials.

- If your basement is flooded, pump it out gradually, draining a third of the water each day to minimize further structural damage. Shovel out mud while it is still moist.

- Hose down furniture and appliances no matter how badly damaged they are as your insurance adjuster will need to see them.

- Make temporary repairs necessary to prevent further damage from the elements or from looters. Keep receipts as you may be reimbursed by your insurance company.

MISCELLANEOUS

- Always remain calm. Seeing your home after a flood can be a shock, but remember, it can all be taken care of. Don't get careless and get hurt.

- Have all electrical appliances, that you even suspect may have gotten wet, checked and serviced by trained personnel before attempting to use them.

- NEVER touch downed power lines or objects touched by the downed wires or go near water moving or standing near them.

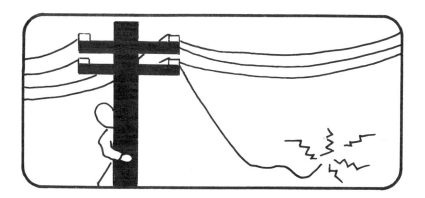

HURRICANES

HURRICANES

A hurricane is a violent storm system averaging 300 to 400 miles in diameter. The structure of a hurricane begins with the core or center, referred to as the eye, which is a calm area with blue sky and soft winds. Surrounding the eye are winds, clouds, and violent weather in varying degrees of severity. The most severe being closest to the eye with winds up to 300 miles per hour, usually accompanied by torrential rainfall. When the eye of the hurricane passes overhead, the winds and rain die down but resume from the opposite direction immediately after the eye has passed.

As the hurricane approaches, the wind and weather conditions build in intensity to their maximum strength. If the eye passes near you, you will experience this extreme violence As the eye passes directly over your area, the violence will die down and you will experience calm, mild weather. When the eye has passed, the violence will resume in full force without build-up or warning.

Hurricanes form in large stretches of ocean heated to at least 82°F. A wind disturbance forces hot, humid air into a spiraling motion. This hot air sucks up more air and as it rises, it cools and gives off great energy. This energy increases the speed of the upward rising mass, sucks in more air and more condensation and releases even more energy. It feeds upon itself until it becomes a huge whirling storm.

The power of a hurricane is immense as it takes in and converts to energy a quarter of a million tons of water every second. Water is by far the most destructive force in a hurricane. Many people drown as tides rise several feet above normal levels.

Aside from drowning people and animals, hurricanes can pick up buildings, boats, cars, trees and other large objects and set them down miles away. They can also make deadly weapons out of harmless objects—a piece of straw can be driven through a telephone pole—besides undermining roads and sweeping away bridges, railroad tracks, and crops.

There are a few terms you should be familiar with so you will recognize them and know what to expect. They are:

- *SMALL-CRAFT WARNING*

  When a hurricane moves within a few hundred miles of the coast, a small-craft warning is issued to warn small-craft operators to take precautions.

- *GALE WARNING*

  When winds of 38 to 55 miles per hour (33 to 48 knots) are expected, a gale warning is issued.

- *STORM WARNING*

  When winds of 55 to 74 miles per hour (48 to 64 knots) are expected, a storm warning is issued.

- *INTERNATIONAL HURRICANE FLAGS*

  Two bright red flags with square black centers or two white lanterns with a red lantern in between them at night are the international symbols for a hurricane.

BEFORE A HURRICANE

In the event of a hurricane, the damage and devastation is so widespread that help may not be available for days. You will need enough supplies to last a minimum of 3 days. To be better prepared stock up for at least two weeks. All of your training (for example, first aid) your family members have had relating to disasters is an advantage at this time.

There are two types of emergency bulletins given to the public, **WATCHES** and **WARNINGS**. In most areas prone to hurricanes or tornados, the television stations will broadcast a **WATCH** and **WARNING** on your television screen. The bulletin is super-imposed on your screen over your regular program and states the nature of the bulletin—for example, HURRICANE WATCH, TORNADO WARNING, a symbol of the impending storm, and those counties affected. (Illustration in section TORNADOS)

PREPARATION BEFORE A STORM

• If there are trees around your home, keep them pruned of dead branches and cut them back so they do not touch the buildings. A very strong wind, such as gale or worse, can whip the branches against the windows and break them, knock gutters and other trim down, and do a lot of other damage.

• If your house is not stormproofed - locate nearby public shelter(s) within a short distance. By following the Weather Service Bureau's warnings and bulletins, you will have time to reach these shelters and safety with the necessary items for the comfort of you and your family.

- Have flashlights, candles, and battery-operated radio on hand. Flashlights and battery-operated lanterns are best used for emergency lighting. Keep plenty of spare batteries and bulbs on hand.

- Kerosene lanterns work well and are safer than candles.

- A battery-operated radio is an absolute necessity. If you don't have one, you will have no way of receiving vital information about the emergency situation if your electricity is out.

- Store extra fuel, water, ready-to-eat foods and emergency medical supplies. (See Section SURVIVAL CACHE.)

- Always keep some kind of covered pail or other container with plastic bags on hand along with some dry bleach for sanitary uses. (See Section SHELTERS/SANITARY FACILITIES.)

- Keep a supply of heavy plastic sheeting, duct tape, and sand-bags to secure first-floor doorways against flood waters.

- Store water-reactive chemicals in waterproof containers. READ THE WARNING LABELS. Chemicals such as carbide produce explosive gases when wet. Dry chlorine produces poisonous gas.

HURRICANE WATCH

A hurricane watch is issued when there is a good possibility of hurricane conditions threatening coastal or inland communities within 36 hours or less. This is the time for you to do the following:

- Make sure your car is fueled. Check battery, oil, and water.

- Gather insurance policies and papers needed to expedite your claim should this become necessary and package them in waterproof containers.

- Store toxic chemicals and fertilizers in the safest section of your home or building where there is no danger they will contaminate flood waters.

HURRICANE WARNING

A hurricane warning is issued when there is a very high probability of hurricane force winds within 24 hours or less. It will identify areas where these conditions are expected to occur. Before a hurricane arrives, take the following precautions immediately:

- Decide well ahead of time whether or not your home will be safe during the storm. If you plan to stay, don't change your mind and try to leave. You will be safer in your home than outside in a car or on foot where debris will be crashing all around you.

- Empty your swimming pool if time permits to prevent it from flooding your home.

- Sterilize containers for storing drinking water including your bathtub and washing machine.

- Turn off water at the main source and follow the advice of the utility company on what to do about service lines. This procedure will ensure that the water already contained in pipes will not be contaminated should water mains break.

- Always turn off the water heater. Water supply failure could boil up enough steam pressure to cause an explosion.

- Turn refrigerator and freezer to the coldest setting.

- Check ready-to-eat food and medical supplies. Fill tub, bottles, and utensils with water.

- Secure outdoor objects that might be blown away such as garbage cans, garden tools, toys, porch furniture, etc. Anchor them or store them inside before the storm strikes.

- Board up your windows or close your storm shutters before the wind starts to blow so hard that it makes it impossible. Cover all glass windows and doors on the first floor with shutters, paneling, plywood, etc., or at the very least, place masking tape 10 to 12 inches apart on the inside of the glass.

- Turn off gas used for your house at the main inlet.

- Unplug all electrical appliances except those that are absolutely necessary such as the refrigerator, freezer, and radio or television.

- Keep listening to the radio or television for storm bulletins and evacuation/safety instructions.

- Family pets should be kept inside with the family. Have plenty of newspaper on hand for sanitary purposes. If you have to evacuate, you should make some kind of arrangements for them. Don't leave them to fend for themselves.

- Keep one window open on the opposite side of the house to the wind to equalize the pressure from the storm.

- Boats:

   Moor your boat securely, then leave it. Do not return to it once the wind and waves are up.

   If small enough, you can remove the engine and temporarily sink the boat; moored, it will be very safe under water.

   Boats left on trailers in the open should be lashed well to their trailers and the air let out of the tires. Tie trailers down to prevent the wind from blowing them around. Remove and store sails and awnings and secure all loose gear.

IF YOU ARE ADVISED TO EVACUATE

- When a hurricane is approaching the coast, the storm tides frequently start rising well in advance of the storm. If it is recommended that you evacuate, do so immediately.

- Put together your evacuation supplies.

- Secure your home and leave in plenty of time to reach safe shelter. It is not safe to be on the road during a hurricane.

- Select an emergency meeting place in case you become separated from family members by blocked roads or high surf.

- Do not stay in a structure that is not sturdy, such as a mobile home or trailer. Turn off electricity, gas, water, then leave.

- Hurricanes moving inland can cause severe flooding. Stay away from river banks and streams until all potential flooding is past.

- Leave low-lying areas that may be swept by high tides or storm waves.

- Plan your time before the storm arrives and avoid the last minute hurry which may leave you marooned or unprepared.

- As you are driving, keep in mind the nearest shelter you are able to reach on foot.

- Avoid night travel.

MULTIPLE TENANT BUILDINGS

- A building security detail should be appointed to coordinate hurricane preparedness activities in multiple tenant buildings.

- Elevators should not be allowed to function during a hurricane. Water may damage the machinery and passengers could become trapped inside.

  Elevators should be parked at the top floor so water will not damage the electrical and mechanical parts if the lower floors are flooded.

COMMERCIAL PROPERTY

- Cover all glass windows and doors on the first floor with shutters, paneling, plywood, etc.; or at the very least, place masking tape 10 to 12 inches apart on the inside of the glass.

- Move all important papers and documents up as high as possible so if the floor becomes flooded they will not be destroyed.

- Unplug all electrical appliances and machinery and turn off the electricity at the main switch to prevent the possibility of fires and electrical shock if the power is restored before you return to your business.

- Make sure that all drains on the roof of the building are clear and water is able to drain so the roof won't collapse under the weight of accumulated water.

- Secure or tie down outdoor signs, particularly the kind that swing.

- Secure and tape glass showcases. Move valuable merchandise as high as possible.

- Secure lumber, machinery, and equipment that are stored in open storage yards or open sheds.

DURING THE HURRICANE:

- Remain indoors during the hurricane. Travel is extremely dangerous when winds and tides are whipping through your area.

- If you are not evacuating, DO NOT leave your shelter.

- Never stay in your car on a beach road if you become stranded. Move to higher ground and seek shelter.

- Stay indoors away from windows.

- If the storm center passes directly overhead, there will be a lull in the wind lasting a few minutes to a half-hour or more. Stay in a safe place unless emergency repairs are absolutely necessary. The winds will resume at hurricane force and will come from the opposite direction.

- When the storm dies, open windows on the opposite side of building as wind will resume from that direction when the storm center has passed.

- Always keep at least one window partially open to equalize the pressure inside the house with the pressure outside.

- Keep yourself calm and try to cheer up the younger and more frightened members of your household.

AFTER THE HURRICANE:

- Stay tuned to the radio for up-to-date bulletins on coastal flooding from tides and inland flooding from swollen rivers and what to do if you need help.

- Remain in shelter until informed by local authorities that it is safe to leave.

- If anyone is injured, treat them as well as you can until you can get proper medical attention. Do not attempt to move seriously injured persons unless they are in immediate danger of further injury.

- If your electricity is off and you are using candles or other open flames for lighting, be very careful as they can easily be knocked or blown over.

- Check utility lines and appliances for damage. If gas leaks exist, shut off main gas valve. Shut off electricity if there is any damage to the house wiring. Report damage to the appropriate utility companies and follow their instructions. Do not use matches, lighters or open flames until you are sure there are no gas leaks.

- Do not operate electrical switches or appliances if gas leaks are suspected. This may cause sparks to ignite gas or other flammable fumes.

- Do not touch downed power lines or objects touched by the downed wires or go in or near wet areas where lines are down.

- Immediately clean up spilled medicines, drugs, and other potentially harmful materials.

- Make sure that sewer lines are intact before permitting flushing of toilets.

- Check refrigerated food for spoilage if power was off during storm.

- Do not use your telephone unless it is an emergency call relating to a medical emergency, fire or violent crime only.

- Do not go sightseeing. Keep streets clear for the passage of emergency vehicles.

- Respond to requests for help from local authorities but do not go into damaged areas unless your help has been requested.

- If you have to travel, drive carefully along debris-filled streets. Do not travel alone if you can help it.

- If you need to signal for help: Put a sign in the window 'SEND HELP'. Think in 3's, the standard call for help—three horn blasts, pause, three more; flash your lights 3 times, pause, flash 3 times again. Repeat in three's.

- If you suspect someone of looting, don't get involved, call the police or other local authority.

NOTES

LIGHTNING/THUNDERSTORMS

LIGHTNING/ THUNDERSTORMS

Lightning is defined as a sudden flash of light in the sky caused by the discharge of atmospheric electricity between two clouds or a cloud and the earth.

Thunder is the sound that follows a flash of lightning, caused by the sudden heating and expansion of air by electrical discharge.

SOME FACTS ABOUT THUNDERSTORMS

- Lightning is attracted to sharp points that are aimed toward the upper clouds such as isolated tall trees, poles, etc. Electrical conductors, or lightning rods protect tall buildings by connecting them to broad bands of metal that discharge the lightning safely to earth.

- A thunderstorm is rain or hail accompanied by lightning and thunder. Although lightning most commonly occurs during a thunderstorm it also occurs in snowstorms, sandstorms, clouds over erupting volcanoes, and even in clear air.

- Lightning can, and often does, strike the same place twice. If your home has been struck by lightning, chances are it will be struck again before another in your area.

- A thunderstorm is maturing if you feel a sudden reversal in wind direction, a noticeable rise in wind speed, and the temperature drops sharply.

- Light travels faster than sound so you will see the flash first. To tell how far away the storm is, count the seconds between the flash of lightning and the thunder. Divide the number of seconds by 5 to give you the approximate distance of the lightning in miles.

BEFORE A THUNDERSTORM

- Listen to local radio and television for instructions and updated weather reports.

- Have flashlights with extra batteries and bulbs, candles and matches (waterproofed), and battery-operated radio with extra batteries on hand.

DURING THE THUNDERSTORM

- Do not stand under or near high objects in the area.

- Do not BE the highest object in the area.

- REMEMBER — Lightning is attracted to and will always hit the highest point in the area. If your hair stands up and your skin begins to tingle, drop to the ground immediately. Lightning is about to strike very close to where you are.

INSIDE

- Do not use electrical appliances or the telephone. Remove plug and antenna wires from your televisions.

- If you are in a building that has been struck by lightning, check immediately for fire. If a fire exists, evacuate the building, call the fire department, and follow the fire safety rules.

- Stay away from all windows.

- Stay out of the bathtub. Do not sit near windows, doors, fireplaces, radiators, stoves, sinks, or pipes. The plumbing system is connected to a vent pipe that protrudes up through the roof.

- Keep away from the fireplace or chimney as these are good lightning targets. Modern homes have networks of wires and pipes running through them. If your home should be struck by lightning, it would probably seek out these conductors instead of you.

- The best place for you to be is in the middle of a downstairs room, away from the walls.

OUTSIDE

- Avoid high objects, tall fences, clotheslines, tall trees, etc. Get out of water and off small boats. Move to a cave, ditch, canyon or under head high trees in forest glades.

- Give artificial respiration if a person is not breathing after being struck by lightning. Do not fear the person as you are in no danger of being shocked by him.

- Never fly a kite in a thunderstorm. You run the danger of being electrocuted.

- Stay away from metal fences, pipes, and railroad tracks. If you are near a water tank or metal tower, you will be protected from direct strokes, but you still can be electrocuted by currents traveling down the tank or tower and radiating through the ground.

- Move into a building or car if possible. Do not get into a small shed, it will provide no protection. If you have a choice, choose your shelter in this order: large metal-frame or metal building, building with lightning protection systems, large building or small unprotected building.

- If you can't get into a building, crouch down in the open away from trees. If only isolated trees are near, get at least twice as far away as the trees are tall.

- Golfers or other sportsmen holding metal rods or wearing metal cleats make particularly good targets for lightning.

- If you are working on a tractor, especially one pulling metal equipment, get off and away from it as they are frequently struck by lightning.

- Do not handle flammable materials in open containers.

- Never take laundry off the clothesline during a thunderstorm. Your clothes may get wet, but you could be electrocuted.

IN A BOAT

- Head for shore as soon as you see the storm approaching. Don't wait until you see the first lightning strike.

- If you cannot reach the shore before the storm reaches you, move into the cabin if there is one, or lie down along the seats. Don't be a tall target for the lightning.

- Don't hold a fishing pole. It can act as a lightning rod.

- Don't jump overboard. Water is a good conductor of electricity.

IN OTHER VEHICLES

- You are safe in an automobile. The rubber tires provide protection.

- Airplanes should always avoid flying through a thunder-storm as they can be dangerously damaged by lightning. Damage can be caused by hail, icing, and turbulence, as well as direct lightning strokes.

AFTER A SERIOUS THUNDERSTORM

- Do not touch downed power lines, objects touched by the downed wires, or any water or other liquid standing or running on ground nearby.

- Check utility lines and appliances for damage.

- Shut off electricity if there is any damage to the house wiring. Report damage to the appropriate utility companies and follow their instructions.

- Check refrigerated food for spoilage if power was off for more than a couple hours.

In most areas lightning is not a major problem. But in a thunderstorm it can be very dangerous. The main things you should remember for your own protection are:

- Stay calm;

- Be watchful and aware of what is happening around you;

- Above all, don't be the tallest thing in the area.

NOTES

NUCLEAR

EFFECTS OF POWER PLANT ACCIDENTS
EFFECTS OF BOMB EXPLOSIONS
SHELTERS
    MATERIALS
    POSSIBLE LOCATIONS
    OTHER SOURCES OF INFORMATION

NUCLEAR

The effects of radiation in our lives is a very controversial issue. We are exposed to low levels of radiation daily that occur both naturally and are produced by man. The danger of radiation is the damage it does to cell tissue.

EFFECTS OF POWER PLANT ACCIDENTS

Concern over nuclear problems is not limited to war. The accidents at Three Mile Island and Chernobyl prove that nuclear accidents can happen with devastating and deadly results.

- The Three Mile Island meltdown caused evacuation for thousands of people, and in many health problems as well as a complete and permanent change of lifestyle.

- At Chernobyl the results are still being tallied with the numbers rising daily. At this time more than 100,000 people have been evacuated from the area. The number of people affected by the radioactivity may never be known.

Radioactive substances give off fast-moving particles that cannot be seen, smelled, felt or tasted. They are invisible but cause damage to cell structure. Depending on the size and extent of the dose some of this damage is repaired by our bodies, but heavy or ongoing doses (radiation accumulates in your system) can cause major health problems like cancer, leukemia, which can lead to death. Your unborn children may also be victims.

Major concerns are with radiation in large doses from nuclear weapons and nuclear power plants. There are many publications, free from the government and for purchase, that give information on shelters, how to build them, and the minimum requirements for stocking and maintaining them.

EFFECTS OF BOMB EXPLOSIONS

In the event of a nuclear explosion, what will happen to you will be determined by how close you are to the actual explosion. When a nuclear bomb is exploded on or near the earth's surface the energy is dispersed as follows:

Percent of Bomb's Energy	How Dispersed
50%	Ground shock and blast waves.
35%	Intense flash of light and intense heat (thermal radiation). It is this thermal radiation that causes instantaneous fires and severe skin burns.
10%	Radioactive fallout.
5%	Released as initial nuclear radiation at the core of the explosion.

The greatest danger would be from radioactive fallout as most of the people in the actual and nearby areas of destruction would be killed immediately or soon after.

SHELTERS

Your best chance for survival would be a fallout shelter whether it is public or private. Learn the locations of public fallout shelters in your community.

If you are concerned about the possibility of a nuclear attack, you may want to build your own fallout shelter in your home. You have several options as to location and materials you can use.

The purpose of a fallout shelter is to prevent as much radiation as possible from getting to you. The three types of radiation we are concerned with are alpha particles, beta particles, and gamma rays.

Alpha and Beta particles Will be stopped by almost any material. The danger with these particles is the damage they can do to the sensitive internal tissues of your body. Try to avoid breathing them. Your shelter must be completely sealed and self-contained for oxygen and clean air for breathing.

Gamma rays The most devastating type of radiation — they can penetrate almost everything. Protection from gamma rays can be accomplished by shielding yourself with thick layers of very dense materials. The denser the material, the more protection you will have.

Our aim is to give you the basics on survival shelters, supplies and information to get you started. A list of publications and organizations that will give you more detailed information on construction, size, type, etc, is included at the end of this chapter.

MATERIALS

Several materials are useful in absorbing gamma radiation. Some of these are assigned a half-value thickness. Half-value refers to the percentage (50%) of the gamma rays absorbed by, and therefore stopped from penetrating, the materials when using a certain thickness.

For Example:
. . . .
300 rems ------ 6.6 inches wood ------ 150 rems
. . . .

The thickness of the given material will absorb enough gamma rays to cut the penetrating dose in half. Some examples of half-value thicknesses are shown below. Keep in mind that each of them will give the same amount of protection:

- Steel — 0.7 inches or 1.8 centimeters
- Concrete — 2.2 inches or 5.6 centimeters
- Earth — 3.3 inches or 8.4 centimeters
- Wood — 6.6 inches or 16.8 centimeters

To know how much of any given material you will need to protect yourself, you must anticipate the dose of radiation you may receive and know what your body can reasonably withstand. Therefore, you need to know a little about units of measurement for radiation.

The unit of measurement important here is called the rem (roentgen equivalent man). It is unknown what exact dose does how much damage to any given person. For example, if the average person receives a dose of 450 rems, he/she would have only a 50 percent chance of survival. They would certainly experience radiation sickness. This sickness is characterized by vomiting and diarrhea, which might disappear after a few days or continue causing exhaustion, dehydration, fever and then death.

If you are lucky enough to survive these first stage effects, you might, within a couple of weeks, experience fatique, loss of hair, hemmorhages on the skin and in the mouth, bleeding gums, ulcerations of the mouth, throat and bowels, complete loss of appetite, weight loss, infections, and anaemia, all progressing over a period of 4 to 5 weeks.

The highest likely dose, outside of some hot spots, is not anticipated to be over 5,000 rems per hour with the dose rate falling off gradually. You would need a half-value thickness of a little over 5 times of whatever material you choose to bring the radiation level down below 150 rems (as shown below) which is the highest dose your body could accomodate without experiencing radiation sickness.

Example:

    (1)   One-half of 5,000 = 2,500
    (2)   One-half of 2,500 = 1,250
    (3)   One-half of 1,250 =   625
    (4)   One-half of   625 =   312
    (5)   One-half of   312 =   156

In other words — if you had to protect yourself from 5,000 rems of radioactive material you would need 5 times the thickness of any of the materials listed to cut the dose to livable requirements.

Some Examples:

MATERIAL	1/2 Dosage Thickness	No. of Times	Thickness
Steel	0.7 in. (1.8 cm)	x5	3.5 in. (9 cm)
Concrete	2.2 in. (5.6 cm)	x5	11 in. (28 cm)
Earth	3.3 in. (8.4 cm)	x5	16.5 in. (42 cm)
Wood	6.6 in. (16.8 cm)	x5	33 in. (84 cm)

Your shelter must be sealed to prevent fallout particles from entering through the air, as well as being carried in by rain water.

POSSIBLE LOCATIONS

Building a separate shelter underground in your backyard is, of course, the preferred way to go. However, this may not be the most feasible plan because of the cost. If this idea fits your needs the references at the end of this chapter will provide detailed information on construction.

If you have a basement in your house, this might be the most suitable place to build your shelter as opposed to new construction. If your basement is underground, you could make do very well with some modifications, in the form of shielding, primarily to the basement ceiling and any basement walls that stand above ground.

An inner room, on the first floor can be modified for use as a shelter. However, without major modifications this would not provide as much protection as a shelter constructed specifically for this purpose.

In any of your shelters there should be a small space with extra shielding. This is where you would spend most of your time after the initial attack until the radiation levels have time to fall a significant amount.

Most of the sources used in researching this book painted a pretty dim picture of what the outcome of a nuclear war would be, either limited or full scale. The psychological effects alone would be devastating. In the long run, it will be your decision on how much preparation you want to make for your family's protection. All preparations that you make will, of course, increase your chances for survival for any disaster. In preparation for a nuclear disaster, you should read the books listed at the end of this chapter. They will help you to gain a better insight into the probabilities of the effects in your particular area.

For information on stocking and maintaining your shelter, please refer to the following sections:

SURVIVAL CACHE
SHELTERS/SANITATION FACILITIES
FOOD
WATER
FIRST AID TRAINING AND SUPPLIES

OTHER SOURCES OF INFORMATION

The following organizations are other possible sources of information:

Defense Civil Preparedness Agency
2800 Eastern Blvd (Middle River)
Baltimore, MD 21220

Committee for Nuclear Responsibility
P.O. Box 11207
San Francisco, CA 92401

Southwest Research and Information Center
P.O. Box 4524
Albuquerque, NM 87106

Natural Resources Defense Council
1725 I Street, NW
Washington, D.C. 20036

Nuclear Information and Resource Service
1536 16th Street, NW
Washington, D.C. 20036

Health and Energy Learning Project
236 Massachusetts Avenue, NE ±506
Washington, D.C. 20002

Environmental Policy Center
317 Pennsylvania Avenue, SE
Washington, D.C. 20003

For further information on radiation, its effects, safety, and health, we recommend the following books and publications:

NUCLEAR WAR: The Facts On Our Survival, by Peter Goodwin, Rutledge Press, 1981.

KILLING OUR OWN: The Disaster of America's Experience With Atomic Radiation. by Harvey Wasserman and Norman Solomon, Delacorte Press, c. 1982.

NOTES

TORNADOES

TORNADOES

A tornado is a violently whirling column of air suspended downward from a dense, towering cloud (called cumulonimbus); looking like a rapidly spinning, funnel-shaped cloud, it starts out white or light in color, turning darker to black as it fills with debris. Its winds have been estimated at over 300 miles per hour, and sometimes have been up to 500 miles per hour. Though it is short-lived, it is the most violent storm nature produces over land surfaces and, in populated areas, the most destructive.

Tornados can be accompanied by violent rain, hail, and lightning before and after the funnel itself. This violently whirling funnel which is almost always seen will usually destroy everything in the path it touches as it dips to the ground. The sound it makes as it dips to earth is a tremendous roar. Observers have also noted a peculiar whining sound like a swarm of bees.

Tornados strike most heavily in the midwestern United States. However, in the past few years tornados have been hitting more frequently in other areas, as far west as Arizona and California. Though they move at a relatively slow ground speed, averaging 40 to 45 miles per hour, they can stand completely still or move at speeds up to 70 miles per hour and damage is immediate and complete. Areas in the wake of a tornado resemble an area that has been leveled by war games. Survival, if in the direct path of a tornado, is a matter of luck unless through preplanning and preparation you can get to a safe place. You have only minutes to get there.

During the month of February tornados are most prevalent over the central Gulf states. The center of activity then moves east in March. They are over the southeast Atlantic states during April. In May, tornados hit the southern Plains states more frequently and in June they move north to the northern Plains and Great Lakes areas and into western New York state.

WATERSPOUTS

A waterspout is defined as a tornado over a water surface, but without the lasting effects or fury of a tornado. When a waterspout goes over land it becomes a tornado, and a tornado moving over water becomes a waterspout.

Formation of waterspouts do not follow hard and fast rules. Their formation begins in all types of weather, most often between May and October in high-temperature areas, such as the Gulf of Mexico, the Florida Straits, the Bahamas, and others.

Generally their ground speed is slow, sometimes a mile or two per hour, but waterspouts have been known to move at torpedo-like speeds, and their size can vary from a few feet to a mile or more in height.

BEFORE A TORNADO OCCURS

There is not much you can do to prepare ahead of time for a tornado, their onset is sudden and violent. If you are in an area where tornados are prevalent, you should have some type of storm cellar. Timewise, tornados move too fast and are too erratic for you to get far enough away for safety.

CELLAR SHELTERS

If you live in a tornado-prone area the U.S. Weather Bureau issues general specifications for building homes that will withstand tornado forces. In the Midwest, the people make underground "root" cellars, which are also used for shelters. Shelter doors should always open inward.

MOBILE HOMES

Although a mobile home is not a safe place for you to remain during a tornado, you can minimize the damage to your structure by anchoring it with cables or tie-down straps fastened into concrete footings, or to anchor screws in the soil.

FORECASTS AND WARNINGS

In the Midwest, weather commonly called "cyclone weather" is a combination of abnormally warm and humid, or muggy, weather. In late spring or summer these conditions, combined with mild winds and cloudy skies, are often signs of tornado weather.

The Weather Service has in effect many hundreds of networks for storm warnings: SKYWARN is a special type of tornado warning system established in 1969 in the Midwest. The National Weather Service alerts SKYWARN to the possibility of tornados. SKYWARN volunteers in turn watch the horizon in their local areas and immediately telephone the Weather Service at the first sight of a funnel. The two types of emergency bulletins given to the public are: **WATCHES** and **WARNINGS.**

In most areas that are prone to tornados or hurricanes, the television stations will broadcast a WATCH and WARNING on your television screen. The bulletin is superimposed on your screen and states the nature of the bulletin, for example, TORNADO WATCH, HURRICANE WARNING, a symbol of the impending storm, and those counties affected.

TORNADO WATCH

A tornado watch is issued when weather conditions exist where tornados commonly have a tendency to form. Tornados have occurred in some states where they are so rare that no tornado watch program is in effect.

When a tornado forecast is announced, this means that one is expected in or near your area. Your radio/TV may be the only advance warning you receive. This is the time to take the following actions and/or precautions:

- Always remain calm. Think of the safest place you can reach in the least amount of time. Keep your children under close observation in case you have to run for it. Now is the time to know the location of all family members.

- Turn on your radio or television (to your premarked emergency channel) for information and instructions.

- If you see any revolving, funnel-shaped clouds and have time, report them immediately to the local law enforcement (Police, Sheriff) or Weather Service.

- Always keep your SURVIVAL CACHE in a place that is most likely to survive a tornado, for example, storm cellar, basement.

- Keep automobile filled with gas.

TORNADO WARNING

A tornado warning is issued when a tornado has actually been sighted or is indicated on radar and may strike your area.

- When a tornado warning is issued, TAKE SHELTER IMMEDIATELY.

- Do not use your telephone to get information or advice (watch or listen to your television or radio). Use the telephone for genuine emergency calls only.

- Do not remain in theaters or gymnasiums. NEVER stay in an auditorium, theater, supermarket, or any other large building where there is a large wide-span roof with little structural support.

- Do not stay in a car, trailer or mobile home.

- Lie in a ditch and shield your head. Cover your face with clothing to prevent dust suffocation.

- Go to the lowest point (basement or cellar) in the house. Get under a sturdy table or workbench, or get into the smallest rooms with the stoutest walls. DO NOT get under a heavy appliance on an upper floor · if the building collapses, you are more likely to be crushed.

- Stay inside building except as noted.

- The safest place you can be during a tornado is as far underground as you can get. If you know the location of any storm cellar and can get there, do so immediately.

- If a storm cellar is unavailable, try to get into a basement and crouch in the southwest corner. Tornados normally come from the southwest. If no underground shelter is accessible, move to a heavily constructed, reinforced concrete or steel-framed building. Otherwise lie in a ditch or depression in the ground.

SAFETY DURING A TORNADO

● *In a cellar or basement*

This is the safest place in a house. Get under a sturdy piece of furniture, if possible.

● *In a house without a basement*

Get in a small room on the lowest level in the center of the house, such as a bathroom or a closet. Get under a sturdy piece of furniture if possible. Stay away from windows as they may shatter.

● *In an automobile*

A car is not a safe place to be. If you don't have time to escape, GET OUT OF THE CAR and move as far away from it as possible. Then lie flat in a ditch, ravine, or depression in the ground.

● *In the open*

Move away from the path of the tornado at right angles. If you don't have time to escape, lie flat in a ditch, ravine or depression in the ground. Be sure to cover your face so you don't suffocate from the dust. A suggestion is to bury your face in your shirt or clothing and try to protect your head with your arms.

- *In a city*

  Get into the nearest small safe building, preferably one with a basement. If there is no basement, follow the directions for a house without a basement.

- *In school buildings*

  Go to a designated shelter area. All schools should have designated shelter areas, if not, contact your school board to get one established.

- *In mobile homes and trailer parks*

  Evacuate and seek shelter elsewhere. DO NOT STAY IN A MOBILE HOME OR TRAILER. They are unsafe in a tornado. Your mobile home park should have a designated shelter and someone to monitor broadcasts during a severe storm.

  If you live in a mobile home, and you do not have time to leave the area, get out of the mobile unit and go to a safer area, even if its only a low spot a distance away.

TSUNAMI/TIDAL WAVES

TSUNAMI WATCH
TSUNAMI WARNING
AFTER THE TSUNAMI

TSUNAMI/ TIDAL WAVES

A tsunami, often known as a tidal wave, is an extensive and often very destructive ocean wave caused by a violent submarine earthquake. A tsunami does not always come in as one gigantic wave, it is usually a series of waves or crests.

As a tsunami crosses the ocean, it cannot be felt by ships nor be seen from the air. The length from crest to crest may be over a hundred miles and the height from trough to crest only a few feet. In deep water, these waves may reach forward speeds of over 600 miles per hour.

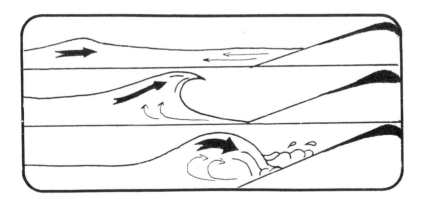

As a tsunami approaches the shore, its speed decreases and the height of the wave increases. They become most dangerous as they crest to heights over a hundred feet and strike with a devastating force.

A small tsunami in one area can be extremely destructive just a few miles away. All are potentially dangerous even though they might not damage every coastline they strike.

If you are in a coastal area the only warning you might get of an approaching tsunami is the earthquake that causes it. If you feel an earthquake and you live in a low lying coastal area, evacuate immediately.

In Hawaii, where tsunamis are more prevalent, information on tsunami inundation areas is available in the green pages of the telephone directory. Become familiar with your area.

Unless otherwise determined by competent scientists, potential danger areas are those less than 50 feet above sea level and within one mile of the coast for tsunamis of distant origin; or less than 100 feet above sea level and within one mile of the coast for tsunamis of local origin, as determined by the National Oceanic and Atmospheric Administration (NOAA).

TSUNAMI WATCH

A tsunami watch is issued when an earthquake of sufficient magnitude occurs in the Pacific Ocean area and alerts the public to the possibility of an approaching tsunami. The term "watch" is used in the same manner here as with other natural hazards such as hurricanes and tornadoes. When a tsunami watch is issued, take initial precautionary measures and stay tuned to your radio or television for further developments.

Sooner or later, tsunamis hit every coastline in the Pacific. If you live in any Pacific coastal area, these warnings apply to you.

Some standard precautions to take if you receive a Tsunami Watch are:

- Cooperate with Civil Defense, Police, and other emergency organizations. They are there to save your life.

- Remain calm. Prepare to evacuate to higher ground as directed by the local authorities.

- Always make sure your car is fueled. Check battery, oil, and water.

- Have battery-operated flashlights, extra batteries, bulbs, and radio available.

- If you have time, take some evacuation supplies. If you live in a coastal area where tsunami's are prevalent, store some supplies now that you may need during an evacuation. Keep them in a place that is readily accessible and in a container that will be easy to handle and move around. See Section SURVIVAL CACHE for specific items.

TSUNAMI WARNING

A tsunami warning is issued with the first positive indication of a disturbance. Along with the warning is issued ETAs (estimated time-of-arrival) for all locations. At this time, local warning, evacuation, and emergency procedures are undertaken.

Evacuate Immediately When:

- The water along the shore begins to recede more rapidly than usual for a normal tide change. The water recedes way out in a short amount of time. *BEWARE -- THE WATER WILL BE COMING BACK IN ONE OR MORE WALL-LIKE WAVES.*

- You are in a known inundation area and you feel a strong earthquake. Don't wait for an official warning from the Civil Defense or authorities in charge.

- Stay out of danger areas until an "all clear" is issued by competent authorities.

 NEVER GO DOWN TO THE BEACH TO WATCH A TSUNAMI. If you see it coming, you are already too late to get out of the way.

The Tsunami Warning System does not issue false alarms. When an oceanwide warning is given, a tsunami exists. A regional warning means a tsunami probably exists.

- Do not use your telephone except for genuine emergency calls. Turn on your radio to your premarked emergency channel.

AFTER THE TSUNAMI

- Stay tuned to local radio and/or television for instructions on where to go for medical attention; necessary emergency assistance for medical, housing, clothing, and food.

- Do not touch downed power lines or objects touched by the downed wires or go near water on or near the downed wires.

- Do not go sightseeing. Keep streets clear for emergency vehicles. In some areas you can be arrested for getting in the way of disaster/emergency operations.·

- If you must travel, drive carefully along debris-filled streets. Roads may be undermined and can collapse from the weight of the car.

- Respond to requests for help from police, fire fighting, civil defense, and relief organizations, but do not go into damaged areas unless your help has been requested. There will be many ways to help yourself and your community recover from the emergency and volunteers will be needed.

- Never eat or drink any food or liquids (including water) that may have come in contact with the water.

- Remain in a safe area until informed by local authorities that it is safe to leave.

VOLCANOES

VOLCANIC HAZARD WARNINGS
TYPES OF HAZARDS
ASH FALLOUT PRECAUTIONS

VOLCANOES

With the eruption of Mt. St. Helens in the state of Washington, we have become more aware of the dangers presented by erupting volcanoes. Mt. St. Helens is not the only active volcano in the United States. It is only one in a chain of volcanoes on a north-south line along the crest of the Cascade Mountains. This chain of active volcanoes is part of the "Ring of Fire," a circle of volcanoes surrounding the Pacific Ocean. There are volcanoes in Alaska, Hawaii, California, Oregon, Washington, and British Columbia.

Concern about potential hazards posed by Cascade Range volcanos led the United States Geological Survey (USGS) to establish a Volcanic Hazards Project in 1967. This project is based on the concept that a volcano's behavior pattern can be determined by studying deposits formed by its past eruptions. It assesses the potential threat of a volcano by a special kind of geologic "detective work." Modern eruptions of a volcano may not affect exactly the same areas exactly the way that a geological study might indicate; such studies of areas affected in the past are, however, the best gage available and are used as a rough guide to the potential impacts of future eruptions.

VOLCANIC HAZARD WARNINGS

The USGS mechanism for assuring that the public and its officials get needed information quickly and in a form suitable to their needs is the Hazards Warning and Preparedness Program developed in; 1976. The program procedures define three levels of geologic-hazard information and notification:

- *NOTICE OF POTENTIAL HAZARDS* — Information of the location and possible magnitude of a potentially hazardous geologic condition.

- *HAZARD WATCH* — Information, as it develops from monitoring or from observed precursors, that a potentially catastrophic event of a generally predictable magnitude may occur within an indefinite time (possibly months or years).

- *HAZARD WARNING* — Information (prediction) as to the time, location, and magnitude of a potentially disastrous geologic event.

Notices are then sent to appropriate local, state, and federal agencies and, through the news services, to the public.

NOTE: These procedures do not apply to flood warnings, even if the floods are related to volcanic activity. Flood warnings, as well as predictions about wind-borne ash distribution, are the responsibility of the National Weather Service of the National Oceanic and Atmospheric Administration (NOAH).

Will Mount St. Helens continue to erupt? The USGS says, "yes." The volcano will probably go through a period of small to moderate-scale eruptions producing ash, pyroclastic flows, and lava-dome growth. No one can predict how long that period will continue or how many such eruptions will take place. Less likely, but not impossible, is another large eruption among the expected smaller ones.

Other Cascade volcanoes will also erupt in the future, just as surely as they have in the past. In the long run they may be expected to erupt less frequently than some other groups of volcanoes around the Pacific Ocean's "Ring of Fire." The possibility still exists, however, that any volcano could erupt again at any time. Although scientists are not now capable of predicting which of the other Cascade volcanoes will be next, the lessons learned from Mount St. Helens in 1980 may allow them to forecast more accurately when a volcano is approaching eruption and to better anticipate when that eruption will occur.

Human reactions to the hazards and to warnings about them are still being studied by the USGS, and the lessons learned will also be applied to future hazard warnings and responses of emergency-services agencies.

TYPES OF HAZARDS

Hazards that continue after a volcanic eruption include possible ashfall and ash clouds, pyroclastic flows, lateral blasts, lava flows, floods, mudflows, and fires.

- *VOLCANIC ASH* is a fine pyroclastic material. It is distinct from the ash produced by common combustion because the rocks do not catch fire and burn during a volcanic event.

- *AN ASH CLOUD* is an eruption cloud containing appreciable amounts of ash.

- *PYROCLASTIC* refers to fragmented rock material formed by the explosion or ejection from a volcanic vent.

- *A PYROCLASTIC FLOW* is the lateral flowage of a turbulent mixture of hot gases and unsorted pyroclastic material (volcanic fragments, crystals, ash, pumic, and glass shards) that can move at speeds of 50 to 100 miles an hour.

- *MAGMA* is molten rock beneath the surface of the earth. When it flows onto the land surface from a vent or fissure it is called LAVA.

- *WATER* from melting snow and ice, and from disrupted stream channels may create mudflows, avalanches, and floods in minutes.

- **FIRES** may be started not only by the heated blast materials but also by lightning activated by the ash clouds.

Eruptions of Cascade volcanoes tend to be much more explosive than those of the well-known Hawaiian volcanoes. This explosive tendency is related to the chemical composition of the magma that feeds the volcanoes and to the amount of gas contained in the magma, and probably also to the shifting crystal plates beneath the Cascade Range. Although the Cascade volcanoes are located only in California, Oregon, Washington, and British Columbia, their activity can affect the entire continent because of the prevailing easterly winds.

The most significant occurance other than the devastating effects in the immediate vicinity of a volcanic eruption, is the ash fallout. The ash can be carried thousands of miles by winds and jetstreams. The long-term health effects of volcanic ash fallout are unknown at this time. However, some basic precautions that should be taken in the event you are in the area of an ash fallout are:

ASH FALLOUT PRECAUTIONS

- Stay indoors as much as possible both during and immediately after any occurance of ash fallout. This is especially important if you have any kind of respiratory ailment.

- If you must go outside, wear a dampened handkerchief or protective mask over your mouth and nose to avoid breathing any of the particles.

- Do not participate in strenuous outdoor activities. This could cause you to breathe in a greater amount of the ash causing possible lung damage.

- Do not eat or drink any food or water that has been contaminated by the ash fallout. Any jars, cans, or other volcanic fallout will not contaminate through packaging. However, any canned, packaged or any type of food that has been near heat, especially intense heat, is questionable.

- To date nothing has been determined about bad effects on drinking water contaminated by ash fallout. However, you should filter any water before drinking. Ways of filtering water are described in Section WATER.

- If you should experience respiratory distress, skin irritation, or any other health-related problem, contact your phycician.

- If you wear contact lenses, you should switch to glasses until the fallout period is over. If your eyes should come into contact with the fallout particles it can cause painful corneal abrasions effecting your vision.

- Don't forget your pets. Try to keep them inside and quiet as much as possible during and immediatley after periods of ash fallout.

- Horses are particularly vulnerable to lung diseases and should be kept in some kind of a shelter and should not be allowed to graze in areas where ash has fallen.

- Avoid driving except for emergencies as this has the same effect as driving through any kind of dust. The particles are picked up and circulated back into the air causing both breathing and visibility problems.

- Ash fallout can affect more than your health. Other precautions that should be taken are:

  - Keep your windshield clean during fallout periods. This requires a lot of attention.

  - Thoroughly rinse any heavy accumulation of ash off the leaves, foilage and blooms of your yard plants. The ash on your lawn will eventually be washed into the soil.

  - Clear the ash out of the rain gutters on your roof and anywhere else it accumulates.

  - Take extra precautionary measures in maintaining your automobile. Air filters and brake linings can be affected.

- To clean anything that has accumulated ash, use a hose and spray the items with plenty of water. Do not rub the surface of the items because the ash has an abrasive consistency and can easily scratch painted surfaces.

NOTES

WINTER STORMS

WINTER STORMS

*A storm is an atmospheric disturbance charac-
terized by strong winds, and usually accompanied
by rain, snow, sleet and/or hail and sometimes
thunder and lightning.*

Many parts of the country are affected by different types of
severe winter storms. Most of them are listed and defined below.
When you hear a weather prediction, you should know what to
expect.

STORM CONDITIONS

BLIZZARD

The U.S. Weather Service defines a blizzard as a storm
having winds at better than 32 miles per hour, temperatures well below freezing (32°F), and visibility is reduced by
snow to below 500 feet.

BLOWING AND DRIFTING SNOW

These usually occur together and are caused by strong
winds blowing falling snow or loose snow already on the
ground into drifts.

COLD WAVE WARNING

A cold wave warning is issued when a rapid fall in
temperature within a 24-hour period is expected. It is
issued to warn the public that greater than normal
protection measures will be required for agriculture,
industrial, commercial, and social activities.

FREEZING RAIN

Freezing rain occurs when it is raining and temperatures are below freezing. The rain freezes as it hits the ground and causes a coating of ice on all exposed surfaces.

GROUND BLIZZARD

This is a term used in the Northern Plains to describe blowing and drifting snow after a large snowfall has ended.

HEAVY SNOW WARNINGS

The U.S. Weather Service uses this term when a snowfall of 4 inches or more is expected in a 12 hour period or 6 inches or more is expected in a 24 hour period.

ICE STORM

Rain or drizzle falling during freezing temperatures (32°F or 0°C) that coats the ground with a layer of ice. It is also known as a "SILVER THAW" in some parts of the country.

SLEET

Frozen rain drops which bounce on impact; sleet does not stick to anything. Sleet can cause hazardous driving conditions when any depth has accumulated on the road.

SNOW SQUALLS

Snow squalls are short but intense falls of snow that are accompanied by gusty surface winds.

WHITEOUT CONDITIONS

Whiteout conditions occur in severe blizzards when visibility drops to zero. This can be a dangerous situation as you can completely loose your depth perception as well as your sense of direction.

WIND CHILL FACTOR

This term is used to describe the effect the wind has on lowering temperatures. There is a very significant difference in temperature when the air is calm and when the wind is blowing. For example, if the ambient air temperature is 40°F with the windspeed at 15 miles per hour, the equivalent temperature is 22°F (below freezing).

Under any of the above conditions driving will be extremely hazardous. Don't travel if you don't have to. If weather conditions deteriorate while on the road, find a place to pull into and stop, preferably near some kind of shelter, store, restaurant, gas station, etc., until conditions improve and it's safe to travel again.

GETTING READY FOR THE STORM SEASON

In your area certain weather conditions will be expected. If you are not familiar with the winter weather conditions, find out from your local Chamber of Commerce, Civil Defense, Weather Service, Sheriff's Department, Fire Department, Highway Patrol, or any other knowledgeable agencies listed in your phone book.

Depending on your winter weather, you should take the following steps to prepare yourself, your family, your home, and your vehicle(s) for the coming weather conditions.

- Make sure your battery-powered equipment, emergency cooking facilities, and flashlights are in good working condition before any storm arrives so you won't be left without heat or light.

- Make sure you have an ample supply of heating fuel, because if your area is buried in snow, fuel carriers may not be able to get to you.

- Stock extra food, water and other supplies as you would in preparation for any emergency situation. See Section SURVIVAL CACHE.

- Have flashlights with extra batteries and bulbs, candles and matches, some type of safety lantern for lighting, and a battery-operated radio with extra batteries on hand.

PREPARING YOUR VEHICLE

Be sure to get your family car winterized. Check the following:

battery	ignition system
lights	wiper blades
brakes	heater
cooling system	defroster
fuel system	lubrication
exhaust system	winter grade oil
antifreeze	snow tires installed
flares	tire and tow chains

By keeping the gas tank filled, you will be keeping water out.

DURING A STORM

When the bad weather arrives, and you are prepared, there is no need to get excited. If you are snowbound and/or unable to travel, stay inside, keep warm, keep yourself and your family members occupied, and follow the procedures listed below as they pertain to your situation.

- Listen to your radio and/or television for news/weather broadcasts. Keep your information as current as possible. The storm can change and bring on new dangers.

- Always listen to and take heed of the latest Weather Service warnings and bulletins on radio and television.

- If your power goes out, use flashlight, candles or lamps for lighting. Be sure to use them safely.

- Prevent fire hazards by keeping your stove, heater or furnace from overheating.

 Never leave your fireplace or any lantern or other type of heating element unattended. If you are in an isolated area, fire can be your worst enemy.

- Unless you are in top physical condition, stay inside during cold snaps and winter storms. Doing any heavy work, like shoveling snow, in the extreme cold and with your many layers of clothing is very strenuous. Don't overexert yourself if you decide you must go outside.

- Protect car from blowing snow.

KEEPING WARM INSIDE HOME OR OTHER BUILDING

During cold spells and winter storms the temperature will drop drastically. The two most significant problems you may have are the expense of heating your home and the possible shortage of fuel, especially when the cold weather covers a large geographical area.

There are a number of ways to cut down your fuel usage and still maintain comfort and warmth.

- Close off all unnecessary rooms

- During the day all family members should congregate in one common area where the heating unit is located, such as the kitchen or a room with a fireplace.

- Limit the opening and closing of doors. Once you warm an area, you want to retain the heat.

- Make sure the windows and heater vents are closed.

- Have the kids "bunk" together to cut down on rooms used.

- Weatherstrip all windows and doors.

IF THE FUEL SHORTAGE BECOMES ACUTE

- Move all family members into one room. Select this room for its versatility, for heating and cooking facilities, and use it for sleeping, playing, eating, everything but bathroom facilities. If your kitchen is very small then try to incorporate another connecting room and close off this area.

- Make yourself comfortable, that's really important. The situation is difficult enough without the stress of being uncomfortable. If you prefer sleeping on a mattress, bring one down and put it on the floor.

 Any type of heating used indoors will take the moisture out of the air. Heat causes the air to become very dry and can cause difficulty in breathing. To counteract this dryness, put some water in a pan and set on a stove or heating unit, or hang a damp towel in the room so moisture is replaced.

OUTSIDE

- When going out-of-doors, wear several layers of light-weight, loose fitting, warm clothes. You can remove and replace layers to prevent perspiring and chilling, and the layers will trap warm air close to your body. The outside layer should be tightly woven, water repellant, and hooded.

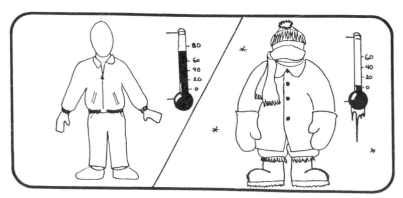

- While outside, cover your mouth to help breathe warm air and protect your lungs from extreme cold. Breathing the extreme cold air can cause harm to lungs and will lower body temperature.

- If the temperatures are freezing outside, be sure to wear gloves and a hat that will completely cover your ears to prevent frostbite. Frostbite will first affect the extremities, fingers and hands, toes and feet, nose, ears, and any other exposed areas of the skin. Also, wear something, such as a scarf, that will cover your neck, mouth and nose to help warm the air as you breathe.

- If whiteout conditions exist and you must leave your shelter, tie a rope or equivalent to your house and yourself, and don't go beyond its limit. You can easily become disoriented and get lost 5 feet from your house.

WHILE TRAVELING

- Don't travel alone – It isn't safe. Take a passenger, and travel with another vehicle if possible.

- Avoid night travel. If you have to travel at night or alone any distance, let someone know where you're going and approximate time of arrival. If you get stranded, you will be missed sooner, and someone will have an idea where to look.

- If you have any doubts while traveling in a storm, seek refuge immediately.

- Always keep planned alternate routes in case the route you have selected is impassable.

- Listen to the radio for the latest weather information and heed any warnings.

- Always fill your gas tank before entering open country, even if you are only going a short distance. If you become stranded you will at least be able to run the heater.

- Always drive defensively. In winter you must be extra cautious.

- Do not drive without snow tires, chains.

- Carry a winter-storm car kit that includes:

Essential Items:

  - Blankets or sleeping bags for warmth
  - Booster cables
  - Fire extinguisher
  - First Aid Kit
  - Flashlight or signal light
  - High-caloric, nonperishable food
  - Shovel
  - Tissue and/or paper towels
  - Windshield scraper

Optional (but recommended) Items:

  - Axe
  - Catalytic heater
  - Compass and road maps
  - Empty can with lid to use as a toilet
  - Extra clothes
  - Knife
  - Matches and candles
  - Two tow chains
  - Bag of sand in case you get stuck

This list is recommended for all travel, but we realize that it is not practical to carry all of the items all of the time. However, for even short trips to the market during the winter ALWAYS CARRY BLANKETS.

IF STRANDED

- Stay in or near vehicle. YOUR VEHICLE WILL BE FOUND BEFORE YOU ARE. Run engine occasionally, but open windows a crack for ventilation. Check exhaust pipe for snow blockage and if blocked and you are unable to clear it, do not run the engine.

- *If out of gas:*

✓ Keep all windows closed.
✓ Turn on domelight at night.
✓ Exercise
✓ Stand watch and do not go to sleep
✓ Only flash headlights to signal to someone for help. Be careful not to run the battery down. If the lights and radio are used unnecessarily, the battery could be dead when you want to signal.

IF YOU BECOME TRAPPED BY A BLIZZARD

- Don't panic. Stay in your car where you are sheltered. You can easily become disoriented in blowing snow. Your car will be found before you will.

- Prevent overexertion and exposure. Pushing your car and shoveling snow are strenuous acts which can lead to heart attacks in extreme weather conditions.

- Always have a source for fresh air while in your car. Leave the downwind (lee side) window open slightly while running the motor and the heater. Check often to make sure that the exhaust pipe does not become buried or covered with snow. This will make the exhaust seep into the car and can cause asphyxiation.

- Exercise by moving your arms and legs and rubbing your hands together to avoid freezing. Don't stay in one position for a long period of time.

- Keep the dome light on at night so the car will be visible. But run the engine for short periods to keep battery charged.

- Make sure one person stays awake to keep watch at all times. If everyone in the car goes to sleep at the same time, you may all freeze to death.

AFTER THE STORM

- Stay tuned to your radio and/or television for news/ weather broadcasts and for instructions on where to go for medical attention, necessary emergency assistance.

- Check refrigerated food for spoilage if power was off during storm.

- If its necessary to drive somewhere, drive carefully along snow-filled streets. Do not go sightseeing. Keep streets clear for emergency vehicles.

- Do not use your telephone except for genuine emergency calls.

- Respond to requests for help from police, fire fighting, civil defense, and relief organizations, but do not go into damaged areas unless your help has been requested. Cooperate fully with public safety officials.

- Do not exert yourself pushing cars, shoveling or walking through snow. Watch for icicles.

- TO SIGNAL: Think in 3's the standard call for help: three horn blasts, pause, three more; flash your porch or vehicle lights 3 times, pause, flash 3 times again. Repeat in three's.

COLD WEATHER HEALTH HAZARDS

HYPOTHERMIA

Your normal body temperature is 98.6°. Everyone naturally worries about it when it rises, but have you ever considered what would happen when it dropped? This condition, called HYPO-THERMIA, can be just as serious as high temperatures.

Hypothermia is the general lowering of the central body temperature caused by more body heat loss than body heat production. The beginning symptoms are caused by fatigue, wet and/or inadequate clothing, combined with overexertion and a lack of high energy food to keep the body warm.

Symptoms of hypothermia are:

- Shivering, a sign the body is trying to generate heat to maintain its normal temperature.

- Exhaustion, apathy, listlessness, indifference, may lag behind if walking, stumble, not pay much attention to where he's going, and is mentally not "with it."

- In the more advanced stage, the person will not know his name, will not answer when spoken to, will be very vague and not really aware of his surroundings. He can show signs of sleepiness, clumsiness, loss of judgment, and may collapse and lose consciousness.

Not being conscious of his condition a person will not realize his danger and may not think anything is wrong. The signs and symptoms can be mistaken for simple fatigue, and neither he nor his companion(s) may realize the need for immediate action. This condition must be recognized and treated quickly—people have died of hypothermia without even complaining of the cold. In fact, the real danger lies in the fact no one recognizes that there is a problem.

The weather does not have to be freezing, you can become hypothermic on a cool day about 50°F, misty or drizzling, with inadequate cover to keep your clothing dry, and not stopping for meals and snack breaks.

Prevention

The best way to prevent hypothermia is to wear adequate clothing for warmth; keep clothing dry; eat regular meals and high energy snacks (for example, raisins, candy, chocolate) to replace the extra calories that your body burns in cold weather; have something hot, soup, coffee or tea with lots of sugar, chocolate; take rest periods often when working or moving outdoors.

Treatment of Hypothermia

Once the body temperature begins dropping, it will continue to drop until something is done to stop and reverse the procedure.

- Find or make a shelter and get victim inside as quickly as possible.

- Change the wet clothes for something dry, at least against the skin, and wrap in dry blankets of any type or into sleeping bag to add warmth and keep body heat in.

- If victim is extremely cold, strip his clothing off and put into sleeping bag or blankets as above, and have a second person strip and climb in with him. The second person's body warmth will act as a heater to warm the victim.

- Do not overwarm the person with extreme heat.

- Use a stove to warm something, if only water, with sugar if you have it, for them to drink—hot chocolate or tea with lots of sugar is the best. The calories will work to warm them.

 Give them something to drink ONLY if they are conscious and not choking and/or vomiting.

- If victim stops breathing, give artificial respiration immediately.

FROSTBITE

Frostbite is the injuring of tissues from exposure to extreme cold. It results when crystals form on the surface or deep in the fluids and underlying soft tissues of the skin. The most common areas affected are the face, especially the nose, ears, cheeks, exposed skin, hands and feet.

Symptoms

The symptoms of frostbite are a sudden blanching (or turning white) of the skin and nose, ear, or cheeks, which may be accompanied by a momentary tingling in the area affected; stiffening of the facial muscles; skin becoming so cold it stops hurting; and skin is soft and elastic.

Treatment of Frostbite

- For the face – place a warm hand over the affected area(s) until the spot hurts.

- For the fingers/hands – put affected hands under the opposite armpits, the victim's or someone elses, as close to the skin as possible, or in a container of warm water (103°F to 107° F) for at least 20 minutes, or until the frozen part is red in color.

- Never rub or massage the frostbitten area and NEVER RUB WITH SNOW.

- Never thaw a frostbitten area unless the temperature can be maintained at above freezing. More damage will be done by thawing and refreezing than if left frozen until warmth can be maintained.

- Keep fingers or toes of affected part separated with sterile strips of gauze.

- Never let a victim with frostbitten feet walk on them after they have been thawed. If the victim must walk for medical attention, the feet should not be thawed.

- Get medical help as soon as possible for any frostbite; even minor frostbite can become serious if it becomes infected.

SNOWBLINDNESS (From Snow, Ice, Sand, Water)

Inflammation and painful sensitiveness to strong light caused by exposure of the eyes to ultraviolet rays reflected from snow, ice, sand or water.

Symptoms

Basic symptoms are extreme pain in the eyes, smarting and scratchy eyelids, headache, and sometimes loss of vision.

Treatment of Snowblindness

- Get the victim into a dark place or cover eyes with dark material.

- Cool compresses applied to the eyes and/or taking your usual pain pills will help to relieve the pain. Time is the only cure for temporary snowblindness; full recovery may take up to 10 days.

- Snowblindness, if not treated, can permanently damage eyes. Sometimes corneal transplants offer the only hope for cure.

- Dark glasses should be worn during any prolonged stay outside in snow or sand. Do not wait until eyes hurt to wear them.

LIVESTOCK PROTECTION

Large numbers of livestock are killed each year during blizzards. Not only for humane, but also for economic reasons, you should take the following precautions for your animals:

- Move livestock into sheltered areas. This is especially important for the young. Shelter belts provide better protection for range cattle when they are properly oriented and laid out than do shed-type shelters where they can become overcrowded and overheated leading to respiratory disorders.

- Stock feeding areas with extra feed before a storm arrives. If the storm lasts more than 48 hours, emergency feeding methods will be required to prevent loss.

- Equip water tanks with heaters to provide cattle with water during long exposure to storm conditions. Cattle die from dehydration rather than cold or suffocation because they cannot lick enough snow to quench their thirst.

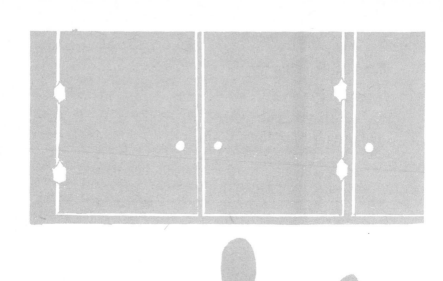

PERSONAL DISASTER PLAN

YOUR PLAN SHOULD INCLUDE:
DRAWING YOUR FLOOR PLAN
FIRST FLOOR
SECOND FLOOR
DISASTER INFORMATION
DISASTER PLAN INFORMATION

PERSONAL DISASTER PLAN

For thorough preparation in any emergency, you and your family should complete a home disaster plan. Having your home well equipped is the first step in preparedness. The second and equally important step is to have your family familiar with the equipment, how it works, its location, the location of safe exits from all areas, and what to do in every type of disaster that could happen in your area.

Your plan should include:

- *A Floor Plan*
  A complete drawing of your home and surrounding yard, that shows the location of your SURVIVAL CACHE™, fire extinguishers, hose, ladders, utility meters, water heater, equipment, and escape routes. To be used in all family drills.

- *Family practice drills for each emergency*
  A family drill should be practiced more than just once.

- *How to get out in a fire? from first floor? from second floor?*
  This should also be part of your practice drills. Include at least one other exit beside the door from every room.

- *A safe meeting location*
  A predesignated safe area located in or near your yard where all family members can meet safely. This may change depending on the disaster - provide for it in your plan.

- *Outside contact for emergency center information*
  A family member outside the area to be an information

center for the welfare and location of family members locally.

- *Closest public shelters*
  Become familiar with your neighborhood. Locate public fallout shelters, hospitals, closest emergency facilities, etc. Learn the fastest routes to these facilities for walking as well as driving.

DRAWING YOUR FLOOR PLAN

The following list is what should be included on your floor plan. Our sample floor plan shows one way to do it. Use it as an example or follow your own inclinations in drawing your plan.

FIRST FLOOR

_____ Doors · exits (2 per room)
_____ Windows
_____ Main walls
_____ Fireplace/furnace
_____ Oven/stove & other type of fire appliances
_____ Yard equipment storage area
_____ Fencing and gates
_____ Water meter
_____ Gas meter
_____ Electric meter
_____ Water heater
_____ Survival Cache™
_____ Smoke alarm(s)
_____ Fire extinguisher(s)

FIRST FLOOR PLAN

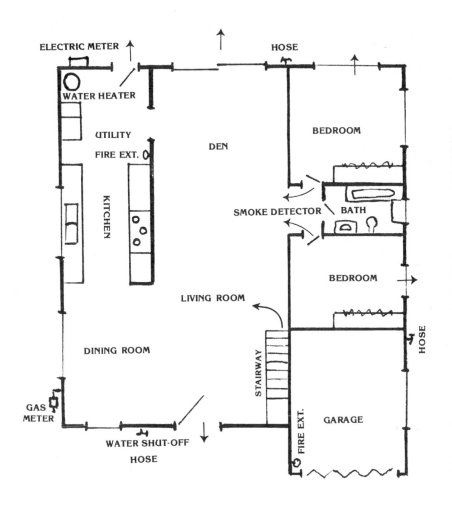

ELECTRIC METER

WATER HEATER

UTILITY

FIRE EXT.

KITCHEN

HOSE

DEN

BEDROOM

SMOKE DETECTOR

BATH

LIVING ROOM

BEDROOM

HOSE

DINING ROOM

STAIRWAY

GAS METER

FIRE EXT.

GARAGE

WATER SHUT-OFF

HOSE

SECOND FLOOR

_____ Fire escapes (1 per room)
_____ Doors
_____ Windows
_____ Main walls
_____ Fireplace/furnace
_____ Ladders for fire escape
_____ Main routes from all rooms
_____ Stairway(s)

DISASTER INFORMATION

Include the information pertinent to your area.

EARTHQUAKES Strongest corner (probably hallway) where the main walls are closest and the family will have the most protection.

FIRES At least one escape route from every room, other than the main door. For second floors, where ladders and hose are located and what route to use.

FLOODS Access to roof if necessary to evacuate that way.

TORNADOES Storm cellar, entrance(s) and exit(s)

HURRICANES Where to store lawn furniture, tools normally left outside, safest area to stay in

Contact your local authorities for suggested agencies, to find out what hazards and probable disasters are a problem in your community. For example, if flooding is a real possibility, find out what areas are most likely to be affected. Check the front of your local telephone book for local agencies.

SECOND FLOOR PLAN

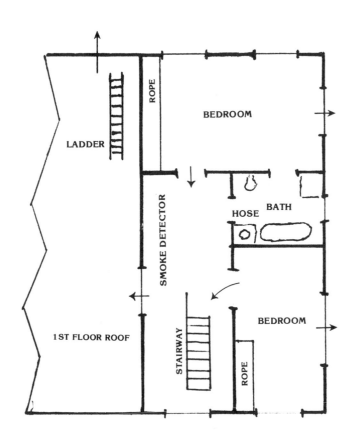

LADDER

ROPE

BEDROOM

SMOKE DETECTOR

HOSE

BATH

1ST FLOOR ROOF

STAIRWAY

ROPE

BEDROOM

Request a copy of your community's local disaster plan. For this, contact your local civil defense agency. If your community has no plan, see what you can do to get one initiated.

DISASTER PLAN INFORMATION

Part of the plan includes a check list for training and special responsibilities for each family member.

No. of family members _____
Who is trained in first aid? _____ _____

_____ _____

List each person and their training. If no one is trained, discuss who wants to go to a class.

_____ _____

_____ _____

_____ _____

Who knows where the utility meters are and how to turn them off.

_____ _____

_____ _____

Incorporate this information in your practice drills.

NOTES

SURVIVAL CACHE™

SETTING UP YOUR SURVIVAL CACHE™
SELECTING A LOCATION
STOCKING YOUR SURVIVAL CACHE™
HOME
PUBLIC SHELTER
PRIMITIVE
IN YOUR AUTOMOBILE

SURVIVAL CACHE™

SURVIVAL CACHE™ is a hiding place or reservoir for storing food and supplies for use during an emergency or disaster.

It is generally acknowledged that the delay in getting assistance to you after a disaster can be as much as 72 hours. However, you should be prepared for two weeks. The magnitude of the emergency will determine the amount of support you may receive from outside agencies. They will be doing their best to get to everyone that needs help; but, depending on obstacles they encounter, there could be long delays. You may still have to survive on your own even after rescue personnel help with life threatening problems. Being prepared to sustain your family will give you the best possible chance of surviving the aftermath of a disaster.

SETTING UP YOUR SURVIVAL CACHE™

Your SURVIVAL CACHE™ is one of the most important parts of your survival preparations. You have the essential items you need to survive stored in one location for easy access and evacuation if necessary.

Your essential items will be complete — you are preparing them now with time for careful consideration so nothing important will be left out. You will have the correct quantities of food, water, prescriptions and other medicine.

If you have your SURVIVAL CACHE™ , there will be less danger to you and your family than if you have to hunt at random through a possibly dangerous building after a disaster when supplies are needed.

SELECTING A LOCATION

The following requirements should be considered when selecting the location of your SURVIVAL CACHE™:

- Choose a sturdy part of your home, preferably in a hallway, in a lower cabinet or cupboard with doors. The doors should have locks or strong latches. (If locked, be sure key is within easy reach.)

- It must be a cool, dark and dry area. This will help maintain the maximum storage life of the food.

- Sturdy shelves are a must. They will be holding many heavy items. Always put heavier items on the lower shelves.

- A piece of wood edging nailed across the front of each shelf will keep your provisions from falling out.

- Your SURVIVAL CACHE™ should be easily accessible to all responsible members of your family.

Other suggested storage places are: 1) a trunk or foot locker placed on the floor of a closet or out of the way in a room (be sure it's out of the sun and away from heat sources), 2) Heavy Duty boxes/cardboard cartons placed in a closet (always on the floor), or 3) large plastic trash can with lid.

STOCKING YOUR SURVIVAL CACHE™

The following lists consist of items to be stored for emergency use. They should be stored in your cache along with the food and water and not be used except for emergencies.

Keep a ledger or notebook containing all the information you need about your SURVIVAL CACHE™. This will be your inventory and you will know at a glance what supplies you have on hand. Information should include quantities, shelf life, dates to be rotated, prescription names and numbers, etc. Figure the amounts of the various supplies your family will need, then plan and store accordingly.

 Any prescriptions or other medicines should be rotated each time you buy them.

HOME

The items in the following list belong in your SURVIVAL CACHE™. In order to handle all of these items easily and quickly store them together in a bag, suitcase, duffle bag, pillowcase, covered box with handles, or something you can move easily if you have to evacuate in a hurry.

CHECKLIST

_____ Aluminum foil, heavy duty
_____ Bleach, chlorinated · small bottle
_____ Can opener, manual
_____ Candles, household
_____ Candy/nuts (in cans)
_____ Eyeglasses, spare
_____ Feminine supplies
_____ First aid book/First aid kit
_____ Flashlight with extra batteries/bulb
_____ Games/books for children/adult

_____ Hand soap
_____ Infant supplies · 2-3 day
_____ Insurance papers
_____ Keys, spare set
_____ Liquid detergent, small
_____ Matches, waterproof
_____ Medication, prescription(s)
_____ Notepad/pencil
_____ Pay telephone change/some cash
_____ Personal grooming items
_____ Plastic bags, large trash
_____ Pocketknife · razorblades
_____ Radio · portable with extra batteries
_____ Rope or nylon cord
_____ Small mirror
_____ Small sewing kit
_____ Toilet paper
_____ Tooth paste/brushes (1/person)
_____ Washcloth and small towel
_____ Whistle for signaling

In addition to the items on the above list, your SURVIVAL CACHE™ should also contain:

_____ Food, canned or dehydrated (see Section FOOD)
_____ Water · 3-4 qts/person/day (see Section WATER)
_____ Pet food/supplies
_____ Additional infant supplies

PUBLIC SHELTER

During or after a disaster, the circumstances may warrant that you stay in a public shelter. If such is the case, you should take with you the "bag" of supplies in your SURVIVAL CACHE™ plus as much food and potable drinking water as you have time to take in safety. The public shelters should provide for your basic needs but anything you can take with you will help ease the situation.

PRIMITIVE

Under severe circumstances it may be necessary for you to evacuate to an area where there are no facilities and little or nothing is provided. In essence you will be camping out in a primitive area. If this should ever occur, you will need several more items to provide for your needs and comfort.

The following is a list of items to be taken in addition to the supplies in your SURVIVAL CACHE™. We feel these items are all necessary — but they should be adapted to your own requirements:

_____ Axe/small saw
_____ Blanket(s)/sleeping bag(s)/per person
_____ Camping stove/fuel
_____ Charcoal/lighter fluid
_____ Clock, battery or spring wound
_____ Clothes for each person
_____ Cooking utensils/silverware
_____ Heavy gloves
_____ Heavy shoes
_____ Insect repellent/sunscreen
_____ Plastic tarps, heavy

These lists are fairly complete, but you may think of something important you want to add to your SURVIVAL CACHE™. Just remember it should be something useful to your survival and comfort in a disaster situation. Some items may seem unnecessary, i.e. games and books; but, in a time of stress such as a disaster produces, occupying the mind is as important to survival as keeping the body comfortable.

IN YOUR AUTOMOBILE

The foregoing information is to help you prepare for a disaster in the home. In your everyday traveling you come across minor situations that could be more easily taken care of with a little prior preparation. The following is a list of items that we suggest be kept in your vehicle for this purpose.

_____ Blanket or sleeping bag
_____ Flashlight, with extra batteries and bulb
_____ Flares
_____ First aid book and kit
_____ Fire Extinguisher (ABC type)
_____ Matches · waterproof
_____ Towels or rags
_____ Plastic trash bags, large
_____ Tools, misc. hand
_____ Water, 1 gallon (drinkable)

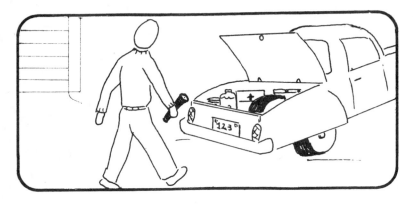

There will be more detailed information for automobiles, boats, RV's, and airplanes in the next book in our SURVIVAL SERIES.

NOTES

SHELTER

SHELTER

A shelter is an area or place that will give you protection from the elements — sun, rain, cold, etc. Whether it is a house, tent, cave, lean-to or some other form of covering, to be comfortable and safe in a survival situation, you will need some kind of shelter.

If your house is unsafe after an earthquake, your first choice should be to evacuate to a public shelter or other place of safety.

In major disaster situations the Red Cross working with public and private agencies will establish shelters for victims. They will provide sleeping accommodations, food, clothing, medical treatment and supplies, coordinate the finding of family members, and provide for any other basic needs.

If the disaster is of major proportions and you are unable to get to one of these shelters, or you are better off staying on your own property but your house is not safe inside, you will need some kind of shelter, especially if it's cold, windy or bad weather.

The maintenance of your body's normal temperature is crucial to your survival and should be of high priority. In temperatures of 50° or lower, if your clothes get damp, without some type of shelter you could become a victim of hypothermia.

Hypothermia is the lowering of your body temperature below normal (98.6°F). For more information and treatment see Hypothermia in Section WINTER STORMS.

ON YOUR OWN

After a disaster, such as an earthquake, tornado, etc., when your house has been damaged, it may become necessary to provide some kind of shelter on your own.

SAFE LOCATION

- Make sure that your shelter is set far enough away from your damaged house, any walls or fences, and/or under power lines that aftershocks from an earthquake, if such be the case, or high winds from a storm, could bring down.

- Be sure to keep everyone, especially small children, away from the house, chimney and other dangerous areas nearby.

- Be sure that the area you pick is free of debris; get all the members of the family to help clean it before setting up your shelter.

- The weather should determine the kind of shelter you will require: if raining, snowing, or damp, be sure you use something that is waterproof — a tarp or plastic cover. Getting wet inside a shelter will not keep you warm.

Do not cook inside your shelter. The safest place is at least 8 to 10 feet away from it. If you are improvising cooking facilities — barbecue, wheelbarrow, or bucket fire as opposed to a campstove — remember to keep the fire small.

SAFETY TIP: Keep a bucket of water nearby when using the fire for cooking, to put out any unwanted fire that may start and to dip burned fingers, arms, etc. into to cool off if such should occur.

MAKING YOUR SHELTER

The following are various types of shelters that can be constructed with materials on hand. Pick the one that will best cover your needs and begin.

TENTS

Ready made — If you have a tent you're all set. Just set it up in a safe area in your yard. If all the members of your family don't know how to set it up, practice now on your lawn or yard. Set it up enough times so that any one of you could set it up with little trouble.

Improvised — For those who don't have a tent ready-made, they can easily be erected by draping a tarp or heavy plastic sheeting (such as paint drop cloth), a sheet or blanket over a clothesline, swing set, rope or heavy cord tied between two trees, two vehicles, two poles or any combination that will support rope and covering. Then pull the bottom edges on or near the ground out to widen the bottom of the tent and hold down with tent stakes, narrow pieces of wood about 1 to 2 inches square and about 10 to 12 inches long driven into the ground, or weigh down edges with rocks or something heavy — any way that is simple and will hold the sides out without putting pressure on the rope supporting it.

Tarps or other cloths draped over a pickup truck bed will make a good sleeping area and relatively comfortable if the weather is bad.

Lean-To — Basically it is just like it sounds, some type of shelter leaning against a strong wall, tree, automobile, etc. If using a wall make sure it is safe and will not come down during any aftershocks of an earthquake, and, if using a vehicle, park in a safe area.

Tie down or connect tarp, etc. to the vehicle, preferably on the far side (that is, over the top of the vehicle) so if it rains the water won't drip down the top and into your shelter. It can be connected by closing it into doors and/or windows on the opposite side of the car or tying the corners of the tarp with cord or something similar and fastening the other ends to door handles, around tires or trees or something on the opposite side of the car that your cord or rope will reach.

Pull the bottom of the tarp out away from the car and hold in place with rocks, bricks, or something heavy enough to make sure it doesn't move. Tent stakes or something similar could also be used. Crawl in and arrange the shelter so it will be comfortable and will stay fairly dry. Hanging another tarp, towel, plastic trash bag, etc. on each end will help keep the warmth in and the wind and/or rain out.

 For good ground insulation for your tent or lean-to use thick layers of newspaper. In lean-to cover with tarp, old blanket, something to hold them in place.

RV's, VANS, TRAILERS, BOATS

Just park in a safe area and pretend you're camping. Sorry, but no campfire unless your fire department okays it. Small barbeques are good for cooking and warmth, but keep them outside of your shelter.

An open boat can be covered with a tarp and will keep you relatively warm and dry.

EMERGENCY SANITARY TOILET FACILITIES

In any emergency situation you should check with your sanitation department, if available, before flushing the toilet. They can tell you whether the sewer pipes are intact or have been broken. If they are intact, there should be no problems with the toilet facilities and flushing. However, if the pipes have been broken or damaged in any way, you should not flush any toilet, to do so would cause sewage leaking into the ground. This is a potential cause of the spreading of diseases, such as cholera, typhoid, diphtheria, etc., that spread rapidly where sanitary rules are not followed.

The following are suggested ways of improvising alternate sanitation methods. Depending on the nature of the disaster and your particular situation, pick the best solution for your needs and plan accordingly.

In most disasters, one of the first things you need to do is turn the water off. This means no drinking water, other than what is stored, and no toilet flushing. Therefore, other sanitary facilities are needed. In an earthquake, you have more choices of facilities because you can use your yard.

- If you have a boat or recreational vehicle with a portable toilet in it, you're all set. Just set it up in your shelter area.

A bucket, pail or some type of water-tight container with a tight fitting lid can be used. A garbage or trash can, bucket or pail will do, but whatever you use **must** have a cover. A small container can always be emptied into a larger one, but they both must be water tight and have covers. Be sure to have a supply of plastic bags on hand and keep one in the bucket at all times. You will need a supply of bags for each container you use for sanitation. You may find a seat necessary for comfort, especially for children and older persons.

OUTSIDE FACILITIES

- If your home/dwelling has any yard, it will be easy to set up some type of outdoor toilet. You might let the older kids, if you have them, set up the outside "bathroom". It will give them something to do and take their minds off what's happening in a disaster. They can be pretty inventive with a little imagination and might surprise you with something unique.

The Teepee and Other Innovations

- Dig a hole at least a couple of feet deep and about one foot in diameter, piling the dirt up around the hole to about one foot away from the edge.

- After the hole has been dug, take 3 poles — these can be tent poles or long boards or sticks at least 6 feet long and with some strength — and lay them together on the ground with the ends even on the bottom. Using a belt, rope, strips of sheet, or anything that can be used for tying and tie the sticks together securely about 1 ½ feet from the top of the shortest one. Stand them up spreading the bottom of the sticks around the hole tri-pod fashion until you get them balanced. Then wrap one or two sheets or blankets, anything large enough to cover the poles, around it keeping the top area where the poles join open for ventilation. Keep one side open for the door but leave an overlap so it can be closed for privacy.

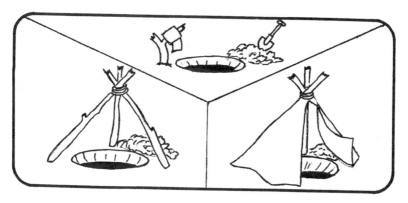

- Dig the hole behind some bushes or near some tree branches (preferably low ones) and wrap a sheet or something similar around the outside of the bushes or drape that sheet, etc., from the limb or part of the tree to make a curtain for privacy.

- Dig the hole near a fence that is stable and not in danger of falling or collapsing, and nail a sheet up keeping enough material on the ground to pull out leaving an open area.

With any improvised sanitary facility it is best after use to cover lightly with something to cut down odor and flies. Some suggestions are:

- Ashes from cooking/camp fire—cooking out you'll have a supply. After they are cold, keep in some type of container so they don't get blown around–plastic bag, box or whatever.

- Dirt—leave some in a pile near the hole with a shovel or scoop.

When it becomes almost full, cover with a heavier layer of ashes, then add 6-8 inches of dirt and pack down so ground is pretty level. Make sure the used hole is filled in adequately, do not leave open. Then move to another location, at least 8-10 feet away, dig a new hole and set up again.

WATER

HOW TO STORE WATER
OTHER SOURCES
METHODS OF PURIFICATION
WATER SAVING IDEAS

WATER

Water is one of the basic and most important necessities for our existence. In any survival situation water that is or can be made potable (drinkable) is more important than food. You can live for two to three weeks without food but only two to three days without water. The first item you must plan for in your SURVIVAL CACHE™ is water - how much your family will need for an extended period of time.

Each person should drink according to their individual need. The average person needs about one gallon of water per day (drinking/cooking).

PLAN AHEAD — ESTIMATE YOUR FAMILY NEEDS AND SEE THAT A SUPPLY IS STORED NOW. Don't wait until you need it. We suggest a three-day supply be included in your SURVIVAL CACHE. This will give you minimum coverage if the other available sources become damaged or unusable.

 Any water that is going to be stored must be purified. Check your CACHE periodically to make sure there is no algae forming.

Purified drinking water can be purchased in 1 and 2 1/2 gallon plastic containers in most markets. The store brand is usually priced lower than name brands and is just as good. Purified water is also available in 5 gallon jugs from distributors. (Check your local telephone directory for listings.)

HOW TO STORE WATER

If you would prefer storing or bottling your own water, the following methods of purification should be used to prevent the growth of bacteria and algae. Always make sure the water you are storing comes from an uncontaminated source and is stored in sterilized containers.

1. Select containers that are plastic with screw-on lids. (1-gallon plastic milk or juice containers are fine.) (Note: Wax-coated cardboard cartons should not be used.)

2. Clean and sterilize the containers by washing thoroughly in soap and water, rinsing well and then final rinse with boiling water.

3. Fill with fresh water and treat with the purification agent of your choice as discussed on the following pages.

4. After filling and adding purification agent, cap the bottle, seal with tape (adhesive or duct is best), and write date on tape.

OTHER SOURCES

When a disaster has disturbed your regular source of water, for example, city pipes or well, there are other sources available.

● *Water Heater*

Your water heater holds 30 to 50 gallons of good water. If the building's water pipes have been damaged you *MUST TURN THE INTAKE VALVE OFF* to prevent the water inside from being contaminated. To get the water out of your water heater, turn the intake valve at the top off and open the faucet valve on the bottom to draw the water. (For diagrams see Section UTILITIES.)

Before extracting any water from the water heater, the gas or electricity to it should be turned off. More recent water heaters have built-in pressure safety valves, but this will ensure that no accidents can happen.

- **Trapped Water**

  A significant amount of water may be available from the water trapped in the pipes of your home's plumbing system if the pipes have not been damaged. To extract this water:

  1. The main water valve must be closed if you haven't already done so.

  2. Next, turn on the faucet that is located at the highest point in your house, this will let air into the system.

  3. Then draw water as needed from the faucet that is located at the lowest point in your house.

- **Melted Ice**

  Melted Ice is a possible source of drinking water if the ice is pure. Two possible sources are ice cubes from your freezer and ice or snow from outside. It can also be melted and purified using one of the aforementioned methods.

- *Toilet Tank*

  Water from toilet tanks (NOT toilet bowls) may be used as a drinking source if NO CHEMICALS have been added for sanitizing.

- *Other*

  Bottled/Canned items: Water is available in many forms from bottled or canned products such as beverages, fruit/vegetable juices, canned vegetables. Milk.

  Some moisture can be obtained from a plastic bag lying out overnight, where it collects dew in the early morning.

- *Waterbed* — DO NOT DRINK WATER FROM WATERBED.

  It has been chemically treated and is poisonous. However, the water can be used to flush toilets.

METHODS OF PURIFICATION

The water must be purified to remove harmful bacteria and other germs that can cause illness or disease. Recommended methods include:

- *Chlorine Bleach*

  For each gallon of water use 8 drops of liquid chlorine bleach where the *ONLY ACTIVE INGREDIENT IS HYPOCHLORITE*. If the water is cloudy, the dose should be doubled. Always stir before storing. Wait at least 30 minutes before drinking. The water should have a distinctive chlorine taste and odor. If you do not detect it by smell, add another dose of the bleach and wait 15 minutes. If the odor is still not present, the hypochlorite may have weakened with age and the water is not safe for storage.

- *Tincture of Iodine*

  Use 12 drops of two percent tincture of iodine per gallon of water. If the water is cloudy, double the dose.

   Use of tincture of Iodine in not recommended for persons with a thyroid disturbance.

- *Water Purifying Tablets*

  There are a variety of tablets (such as **Halizone, Coughlans**) available in sporting goods and drug stores. Follow the manufacturers's directions for recommended dose. Double the dose if the water is cloudy.

- *Boiling*

  There are discrepancies in the many sources as to length of boiling time. Recommendations range from 15 to 30 minutes. The water will taste flat but flavor can be improved with aeration (see illustration).

  Although the water you have stored is perfectly safe to drink, it may have a funny taste from being stored for a long period of time. The taste can usually be improved by aeriation. To do this, simply pour the water back and forth from one container to another several times.

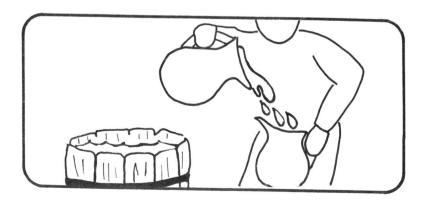

Before using water contaminated with dirt or other small particles you must strain it through a paper towel or several thicknesses of clean cloth.

Allowe the water to settle in a container for ± 24 hours. After the solid particles have been removed, boil the water for 15 - 20 minutes or add a water purifying agent per above suggestions.

If you have any prior warning and time allows, try to store some water. The fastest way is to fill the bath tub, washing machine, pails or buckets and plastic containers, pots or anything that will hold water. Keep checking on the water as it comes out of the faucet. If it turns color or has an odor to it, **STOP FILLING IMMEDIATELY. It may be contaminated. DO NOT USE** any of the water in the container you were filling for consumption. Save it, but mark it so no one will drink it, and use it for flushing the toilet.

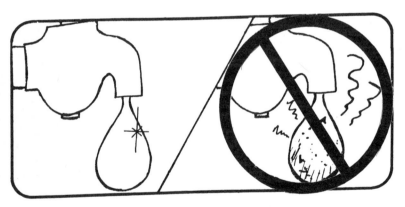

WATER SAVING IDEAS

It is possible to reuse water. If you are running low, keep in mind that:

- If the sewer pipes are intact, you can use dirty water to flush the toilet because they work on a gravity principle. This will help you save the good water in the pipes for drinking, cooking and other uses.

- Conserve water by limiting toilet flushings.

- The dish rinse water is okay for washing clothes or hair, and then using to flush toilet.

Water is the most important of your basic needs. If you are in a hot climate, or are doing a lot of strenuous work, your body needs more water, don't ration it by limiting your consumption. Your body needs that water to stay healthy. If you must conserve water, you can limit use and ration it in many other ways, but drink all the water your body craves.

FOOD

FOOD

The consumption of food is a daily activity that most of us take for granted. Little time is spent on planning how to prepare our food should we be suddenly deprived of our modern conveniences. It is important to plan what your family will eat and how it will be prepared when a disaster that interrupts your normal living pattern occurs.

Enough food should be stored to sustain your family for a two-week period. The following are some suggested guidelines for the selection and storage of food for your SURVIVAL CACHE.

Factors to take into consideration when planning your food are:

✓ quality-taste   ✓ flavor
✓ cooking time   ✓ variety
✓ ease of preparation   ✓ use of preservatives
✓ nutritional value   ✓ price

TIPS TO USE WHEN BUYING FOOD

- Buy the size your family will use at one meal. You don't want to mess with leftovers.

- Make sure you have some of the foods your family likes and eats regularly.

- When planning your shopping list, and storing food, plan for one pot meals, i.e., stew, rice dishes, so you don't waste water on clean-up.

Records should be kept so that you know what foods are on hand and what foods need replenishing in survival storage and freezer. This will keep you from storing food too long.

DO NOT use or buy foods if any of the following signs are present:

- Bulging of the top or bottom of the can

- Discolored side seams, or any sign of seepage

- Off-odor or foamy when the can is opened

- Any unusual milky quality of liquid

- Any food that has not been refrigerated below 45° may be considered to be slightly spoiled

- Don't use leftover food if discoloration, off-odor or mold can be detected.

TYPES OF FOOD AND PACKAGING

CANNED:

Has a shelf life of 1 to 2 years. Rotate stock every 6 to 12 months to ensure freshness. Most canned and packaged foods are code dated, check with your grocer if you don't understand the code dating.

Tips for canned foods:

Vegetables and Fruits: Good · can be used as extra source of liquid

Meat—tuna, beef: Good · keep rotated so no spoilage

Meat dishes—hash, chili, spaghetti, stew: Good variety and size choices · keep rotated so no spoilage

Soup, canned: Quick, easy to prepare, can eat cold, condensed and ready-to-serve.

DRY FOODS:

Long shelf life when stored properly · up to 2 years. Must be sure they are in airtight containers so bugs cannot get in.

Tips on Dry Foods:

Pasta, rice: Good staple for one-pot meals can add meat, vegetables, eggs, just about anything. Needs water for cooking.

Pkg soup mix: Cooked can be eaten as is or mix with canned vegetables or meat. Good one-pot meal

Soup, dry, instant: Quick, easy to prepare, must add water. In cold weather, good for fast warming up.

Dried soup mixes: Will store well when air-tight, add or mix with almost anything.

FREEZE DRIED

Long shelf life; variety; need to add water to prepare; most can be prepared in own packaging or one pot.

Tips on Freeze Dried Foods:

Dehydrated eggs: Add water, seasonings, standard egg taste

Powdered milk: Good staple · need to add water; use to cook, drink

RETORT FOODS

A relatively new way of packaging food now on the market with an exceptionally long shelf life—at least 5 years (tested) without rotating. Each meal is packaged complete with liquid and can be heated in salt or contaminated water as long as the package remains sealed and the outside is wiped clean before opening.

Tips on Retort Foods:

A variety of meals, precooked so can be eaten hot or cold, are put out by a few manufacturers. Main source: some markets, mountaineering stores. One brand, Yurika, is sold by private distribution.

FOOD-USING SEQUENCE

1st   Use perishable foods · from refrigerator

2nd   Use freezer foods (a list on the outside of freezer will cut down door-opening and keep contents cold longer)

3rd   Use staples and nonperishable foods

PREPARING AND PACKAGING FOOD FOR STORING

Keep foods in the coolest, driest and darkest spot available in your house. Keep food covered at all times—when opening them, do so carefully so they can be reclosed.

Be sure to put label or piece of tape on every container with information that includes contents and date sealed.

FOOD SHELF LIFE / PREPARATION TABLE

	Shelf Life	Pre-cooked	Eaten Cold	Eaten Heated	Prep Time (Minutes)	Needs Liquid
CANNED						
Fruits	18 months	X	X	X		
Meats	18 months	X	X	X	5-10 min	
Milk	6 months		X	X	0-5 min	X
Seafood	12 months		X	X	5-15 min	
Soups	6 months	X	X	X	5-10 min	X
Stew, hash, etc.	18 months	X	X	X	5-10 min	
Vegetables	18 months	X	X	X	5-20 min	
Citrus fruits	6 months	X	X			
Juices	18 months		X			
Citrus juices	6 months		X			
Berries	6 months	X	X	X	0-5 min	
Nuts	12 months		X			
DEHYDRATED/FREEZE-DRIED						
Eggs	20 years	X		X	5-20 min	X
Fruits	20 years	X	X	X	5-15 min	X
Meats	20 years	X		X	5-20 min	X
Stew, hash, etc.	20 years	X		X	5-20 min	X
Spaghetti, chili	20 years	X		X	5-20 min	X
Soups	20 years	X		X	1-10 min	X
Vegetables	20 years	X		X	5-20 min	X
DRIED						
Fruits	6 months	X	X	X	5-20 min	X
Soups	2 years +	X		X	5-60 min	X
Vegetables	2 years +	X		X	5-60 min	X
Legumes	18 months	X		X	5-20 min	X
Fruits	6 months	X	X	X	5-20 min	X
DRY						
Hot Cereals	12 months	X		X	1-10	X
Cold Cereals	12 months	X	X			X
Pasta Noodles	12 months	X	X		5-20	X
Powdered Milk	6 months		X		X	
Coffee, tea	12-18 mos			X	1-5	X
Chocolate	12 months	X		X	1-5	X
Potatoes	1 year +		X	X	5-25	X
Rice	1 year +			X	5-25	X
RETORT						
Entrees, variety	5 years+	X	X	X	5-20 min.	

- The shelf life of dehydrated foods will be 20 years only as long as the packages remain unopened and intact.
- Cooking times are approximate; if you feel something should be cooked longer then do so.
- All items that can spoil must be rotated often enough to insure they stay good. Just storing the items is not enough—when sometime in the future you suddenly need them you must know they will be usable.

FOOD STORAGE

Flour, sugar, powdered milk, dried foods (i.e., rice, pasta, split peas, beans), raisins, nuts, and other fruits, etc., can be stored in the following to keep them bug-free.

- *Coffee Cans: 1, 2, or 3 pound cans w/plastic lids.* Fill with powdered, dry items then close with plastic lid and tape shut to seal air-tight. Mark.

- *Jars w/screw top lids.* Fill with dry products then screw tightly to seal air-tight and mark contents and date sealed.

- *Tupperware or other plastic containers that have air-tight fitting lids.* Fill with powdered or dry items then close with plastic lid, tape shut to seal and mark contents.

- Bread, crackers, etc. wrapped and closely sealed in plastic bags or air-tight containers will keep fresh.

COOKING — ALTERNATE WAYS

 Before using any of the following methods of cooking, make sure that an area of at least 10 feet in diameter is cleared of anything that will burn, and the area is well ventilated.

INSIDE:

We do not recommend cooking indoors on other than approved stoves/ovens. The one exception could be a fireplace but ONLY if you make sure area around the hearth is completely clear of all furniture, papers, wood supply, anything that might burn.

OUTSIDE:

Before setting up your fire, pick a location, easily accessible but out of the main line of traffic. Make sure the area is cleared of flammable materials. Watch out for wood or other burnable furniture, clothes lines, trees or bush branches hanging down or near fire area.

- RV or camping stove: butane/propane · use in RV or camper if built in, or in well ventilated area

- Barbeque or hibatchi: use charcoal or wood (Charcoal lighter needed)

- Fire in Wheelbarrow · Charcoal or wood · (put in yard or driveway)

- Trench or hole fire in safe area of yard. An open fire should be cleared ten feet all the way around.

UTENSILS TO KEEP ON HAND

2 POTS — small or medium and large

BUCKET — next to fire area filled with water when cooking in case of burns or fire.

TIPS FOR EASIER COOKING

- Keep a supply of plastic cooking bags on hand. When cooking your meals, you can put the food into a plastic bag with the necessary amount of liquid added, and then into a pot of water. As the water heats up it will also heat the food in the bag. (Keep the top from getting extra water into it.) When the food in the bag is hot, take the bag out and serve the food.

  You will now have a pot of hot water to use for coffee, tea, instant soup, etc., and the pot is clean.

- Foil Dinners: These simple dinners are easy to make, very nutritious and require a minimum of clean up. Start with any combination of the following vegetables: potatos, carrots, zuccini, cauliflower, green beans, broccoli, onions, etc. It is better to use raw vegetables. Add a piece of meat, hamburger, pork chop, chicken, etc. Meat is optional. Add a little seasoning salt and a dab of butter. Wrap it all up in individual servings in aluminum foil making sure it is sealed all the way around. Then wrap it one more time. Cook in charcoal, fireplace, oven, etc. for 15-20 minutes, turn and cook 15-20 minutes, and turn one more time and cook another 15-20 minutes. Take out and eat directly out of the foil or put on a plate. These meals retain all of the vitamins and nutrients because no water is added and nothing escapes. For cleanup, just throw foil away and wash silverware. You can keep the foil used on the outside and reuse it.

- Coat the outside, bottom and lower sides, of your cooking pans with a little bit of liquid soap so any black from the fire will wipe right off.

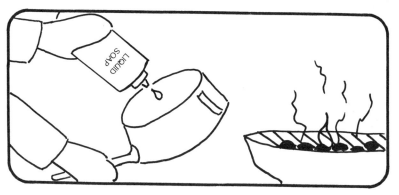

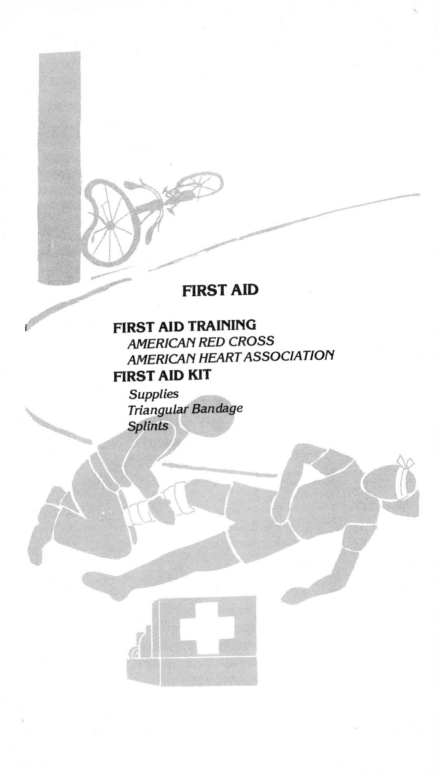

FIRST AID

FIRST AID TRAINING
AMERICAN RED CROSS
AMERICAN HEART ASSOCIATION
FIRST AID KIT
Supplies
Triangular Bandage
Splints

FIRST AID TRAINING AND SUPPLIES

In any emergency or disaster the probability of injury is always present. In a disaster of any proportions medical aid may be delayed in getting to you. Any training or expertise you or your family has will certainly enhance your chance for survival should someone be injured.

The following describes the medical aid (first aid) training classes available to anyone interested and the agencies that offer them. It also includes a list of suggested supplies to have on hand, however once you've had some first aid training you may want to modify it to your own special needs.

AMERICAN RED CROSS

Some of the first aid classes offered and taught by the American Red Cross are listed below. They also offer courses in earthquake preparedness; family health; swimming and life-saving; boating safety and fun; plus courses for young people. Their Red Cross Course Catalog has a complete listing of courses and descriptions. Check with your local chapter for more information.

Basic Aid Training
Essentially designed for the fourth grade school children to be taught in a classroom setting. (Course length · 6 hours)

Standard First Aid – Multi-Media
Modular concept with films, reading and actual practice. Prepares people to care for injuries and to meet emergencies while medical assistance is on the way. (Course length – about 7½ hours)

Standard First Aid

Covers the same material as multi-media using the modular system, classroom lecture-type setting. Incorporates more hands-on practice. (Course length – about 15 hours)

Advanced First Aid and Emergency Care

Takes approximately 53 hours of course work, is an intensive course that is designed essentially for people that have special interest or need for these particular kinds of skills, such as search & rescue, volunteer firemen, school athletic trainers, etc. This is an in-depth study of first aid techniques, but is not a professional course. It is for non-medical professionals and does not qualify anyone for fire, paramedic or ambulance professional positions.

Cardiopulmonary Resuscitation (CPR)

Teaches the techniques of combining mouth-to-mouth resuscitation with external cardiac compressions to restore breathing and heartbeat in cardiac arrest victims and first aid for foreign body obstructions of the airway. Lectures, descriptions and practical work. (Course length: lecture - 8 hours, Modular - 7 hours)

Most Red Cross chapters also have courses in coping with disasters designed to deal with the local situation and prospective disaster. They also have disaster courses for community volunteers including disaster action team training, shelter management, mass feeding, damage assessment, among others.

AMERICAN HEART ASSOCIATION

Provides CPR courses which are equivalent to the Red Cross and well taught in their own right. The training incorporates the use of prepared films, workbooks and practical work.

Other groups that offer courses on disaster training include Office of Emergency Services (OES), National Guard, Coast Guard and Civil Defense. For more information on trainings or opportunities for local volunteer work contact your local office of any of the above mentioned groups.

Emergency Medical Technician Classificatio.

The EMT course is primarily for emergency pers\
given through community colleges and private sci.
regulations to practice professionally may vary from state
and from county to county. For example, in California the c
is state certified, and takes 96 hours, plus another 32 hour. in
Ambulance or Fire Science. To get the details for your area, call
your local Fire Department, Office of Emergency Services, or
community college.

FIRST AID KIT

Your first aid kit is an important part of your SURVIVAL CACHE
and should always be kept well stocked, clearly marked, and dry.
It should include the following:

Supplies

Item/Description	Quant.	Notes
Bandages, sterile roller, 2"	2	Add 1/family member
Bandages, roller, sterile, 4" wide	1	Add 1/family member
Band aids/plastic strips, misc.	50	(1 box)
Bandages, large triangular	3	See illustration below
Gauze pads, 2" x 2"	25	Add 10/family member
Gauze pads, 4" x 4"	5	Add 5/family member
Adhesive tape, roll, 2"	1	Can be cut narrower
Cotton, sterile absorbant	1 box	Bag of cotton balls ok
Q Tips or similar applicators	1 pkg.	(optional)
Antiseptic solution	1 btl	Bactine, Betadine, other
Aspirin or other analgesic	1 btl.	Regular family's brand
Alcohol, rubbing	1 btl.	
Petroleum jelly or Vaseline	1 jar	Prefer water soluble
Scissors	1 pr	Small, blunt ends preferred
Tweezers	1 pr	Pointed, if possible
Needles, sewing	2-3	For splinters
Safety pins, assorted sizes	10	
Thermometer	1	Regular or rectal
Soap	1 bar	
Sanitary napkins	1 doz.	Can be large bandages
Small hand towel	1 - 2	
Mineral oil	1 btl	Small
Prescription medicine	2-weeks	Rotate each time you buy
Prescription glasses	1 pr/	
Bleach	1	Sm. btl or box
Sticks (like popsickle)	4-6	Splints - finger

First Aid Book — Just having the first aid kit ready and available is not enough. To be really prepared, you or some member of your family should have the knowledge and training to use them effectively when needed. The more family members trained and the more training you have the better prepared you are.

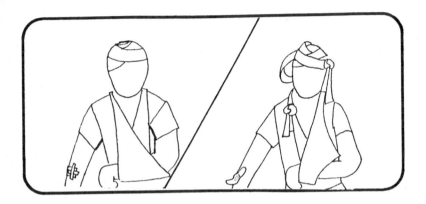

Triangular Bandage

This is the most versatile and most important bandage you could use. It is used to tie on splints / immobilize limbs, and hold them in place, hold on dressings, compresses, bandages, use as a sling, and many other uses.

How To Make Triangular Bandages

✓ Start with a clean piece of cloth, cut into pieces 38" x 38" (square). The cloth should be light colored (muslin, cotton or line are best), an old sheet or tablecloth will do, be sure it is clean. Fold each square in half diagonally and cut along the diagonal fold. (Figure 1)

To Fold:
1. Fold point C to midpoint of AB side. (Figure 2)

2. Fold again in half the same way. (Figure 3)

3. Fold a third time the same way. (Figure 4)

4. Fold in half (width) and roll up tightly starting with center fold. Secure with rubber band or tie with string.

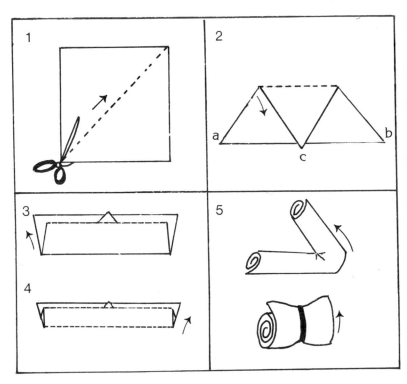

Splints

There are many kinds of splints for sale, however it is not necessary to have regular splints in your first aid kit as they can be improvised from many items around your home.

What you need is something that is 1) strong enough to keep its shape without bending or breaking, 2) long enough to cover the break and both joints, above and below it, and 3) wide enough to protect the injured limb. Suggested items are: magazine, rolled newspaper, board, lightweight metal. Make sure any rough edges are well padded before using.

UTILITIES

KNOW YOUR METERS
GAS
PROPANE
WATER
ELECTRICITY

UTILITIES

In the event of any disaster, where a utility may malfunction or be damaged, your gas, electricity, and water can cause significant problems and even become a threat to your life. For example, in an earthquake, your gas lines may rupture causing an extreme danger of explosion; broken water mains can cause flooding and lack of fresh water to your home; and damaged wiring can cause fires. Therefore, it is important to know your utilities.

The first step is to familiarize yourself and your family members with the gas, water, and electric meters, their location, what to do if there is ever a problem, where the tools are kept, and when and how to turn them off and on.

You need to know this information when:

- you enter your home and smell gas or something burning that could be electrical.

- you are evacuating before a hurricane.

- after and earthquake, when you smell gas, or see smoke.

- you receive a flood or tsunami warning.

- In any emergency where it becomes necessary to shut of your utilities.

GAS

Find your gas meter. In most instances, it will be located along a side wall on the outside of your home. It is usually painted gray and similar to that in Figure 1. If you cannot find it, there are several other places to look since there is no specially designated location for meters.

FIGURE 1

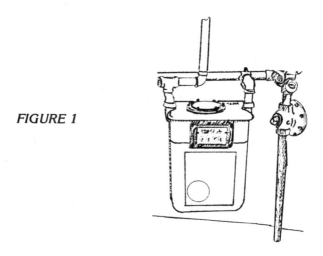

- In some large older buildings, the ,meters were put in the basement. Some were also put under the house but most have since been moved.

- Curb meters were used in some locations before 1945. Most gas companies had stopped putting them there after that time, but in the last few years, some companies started installing them at the curb again.

- Access to the individual meters can be in several locations around your home. Normally, the location is dictated by the builder. A newer practice is to locate meters inside small boxes inside and along a wall of the garage. If you still cannot locate your meter, call your gas company to help locate it.

- Meters from 1965 and up are similar — square or round. On/off valves are the same or work on the same principle, See Figure 2

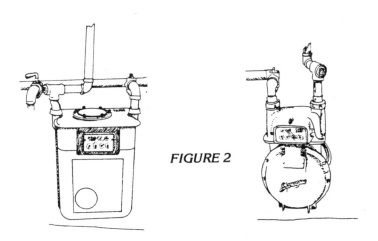

FIGURE 2

When you have found your gas meter, check it carefully and locate the INLET side and the switch/valve that opens and closes the pipe where the gas comes in. See Figure 3.

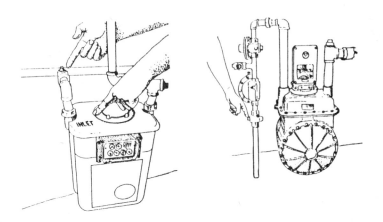

FIGURE 3

There are three ar four standard types of valves. The valve is attached to a disc-type baffle shaped to fit the inside of the pipe. The length of this valve runs the same direction as the baffle inside.

Valves are marked on top for open and closed (see Figure 4). The gas is OFF when the valve is turned crossways (perpendicular) to the pipes. The switch may turn either to the left or to the right but it should turn only 90° in one direction. To turn the valve, you will need a crescent wrench. You should keep one attached to or near your meter at all times.

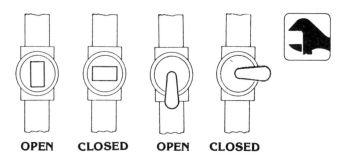

OPEN   CLOSED   OPEN   CLOSED

FIGURE 4

Don't try to turn your gas off — If it gets turned off accidently, all of your pilot lights will have to be relit. You can do this yourself if you know what you're doing. Follow the directions on the equipment. If your heaters and other appliances are in good conditon there should be no problems with the safety valves. If you need assistance, your local gas company will come out and check and relight them.

PROPANE

If your home uses propane rather than natural gas, you should have a tank outside. Your tank may or may not have a meter, but it should have a shut-off valve. To turn off the gas, simply turn the valve in a clockwise direction until it stops. If you're not sure where the shut-off valve is, call your distributor and ask.

WATER

Find you main water intake valve. Most water main valves are located adjacent to the water meter on the curb or near the street. Some are located on a pipe directly attached to your house or building. To shut off the water intake to your home, turn the main intake valve, commonly called a "gate valve," in a clockwise direction until it stops. Know how to shut your water off.

ELECTRICITY

Most electric meters are located about four feet up on an outside wall of your home or building and your main electrical switch should be located in a box right under your meter. Inside this box, you will have fuses (older houses or buildings), square buttons, or switches (circuit breakers). Fuses must be pulled or unscrewed depending on the type. If you do not know what kind of fuse it uses, find out and keep some spares on hand. Buttons push on and off. Circuit breakers flip up, down or sideways. Know in advance of an emergency how to turn your electricity off.

The following figures show you how to turn your main electrical switch, water supply, water heater intake valve off, and also what to do to save the water that is in your house pipes and water heater.

A. *Fuses: pull or unscrew to change.*

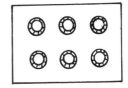

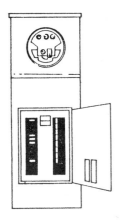

B. *Square Buttons: push on/off*

C. *Switches: Circuit breakers, flip up, down or sideways.*

Water heater and its main components.

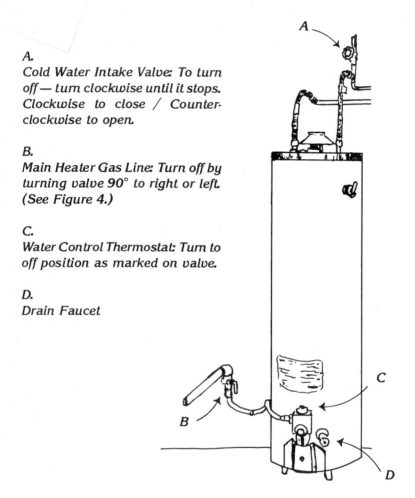

A.
Cold Water Intake Valve: To turn off — turn clockwise until it stops. Clockwise to close / Counter-clockwise to open.

B.
Main Heater Gas Line: Turn off by turning valve 90° to right or left. (See Figure 4.)

C.
Water Control Thermostat: Turn to off position as marked on valve.

D.
Drain Faucet

To remove water from water heater first turn off the intake faucet (see A. above) to prevent any contaminated water from going into heater. Then turn off gas (see B. above) or electricity, if electric heater. Turn on a hot water faucet somewhere in home so air can flow back into heater to displace water. Before opening drain faucet (see D. above) be sure to have a bucket, or receptacle under faucet to catch water.

NOTES

COMMUNICATIONS

STORM BULLETINS –
WATCHES AND WARNINGS
RADIO COMMUNICATIONS
OTHER EQUIPMENT
    RADIO RECIEVERS (receive only)
    TELEVISION SETS
    SHORTWAVE SCANNER RECEIVERS
RADIO TRANSCEIVERS (send and receive)
  No License Required
    WALKIE-TALKIES
    COMMUNICATORS
    CITIZEN BAND (CB) RADIOS
RADIO TRANSCEIVERS - License Required
    MARINE AND AVIATION RADIOS
    GENERAL MOBILE RADIO SERVICE (GMRS)
    AMATEUR RADIO
    FOR TRANSCEIVERS

COMMUNICATIONS

Communications is the link between people, the transmitting of information or an idea from one person to another, one place to another. Communication takes many forms from sounds of drums deep in the jungles to radios and televisions around the world via satellite.

Communication is a necessary part of survival during any type of disaster or local emergency. With the advent of a disaster, radio and television are the only contact you may have with the outside. If there is a power outage in your area, that portable radio and extra batteries will be your only link to what has happened and what you can do to help yourself, your family, friends and neighbors.

In today's society, a standard way to alert people of an impending disaster is with the use of sirens. When sirens sound in steady tones for 3-5 minutes, it is to alert the population of that area that an emergency is imminent or has already occurred.

Check your local community through its service agencies. Learn what kind of warning systems are used and the signals that are used for each type of emergency. When you hear a warning signal, immediately tune to your local radio or television station. Listen carefully and do what is suggested.

When you have been alerted, you need to know:

A.   What is happening,

B.   Where to go for shelter or protection,

C.   The whereabouts of your family

D.   What help and services are available after the disaster

E.   Where to go for help that you might need.

YOU SHOULD NOT. . .

. . . . use the telephone, unless it is an emergency. Use only for police, medical, fire.

. . . . go sightseeing. You can get in the way of emergency vehicles (depending on the emergency you can be arrested for just being in the area).

The television and radio stations will be giving up-to-the-minute information.

STORM BULLETINS:
WATCHES AND WARNINGS

WATCHES: During any natural disaster the radio and/or television will broadcast a WATCH (for example, tornado watch, hurricane watch, etc.). This is to inform you that the weather conditions are right or building for that particular danger.

WARNING: Broadcast when the actual natural disaster has been spotted and you are in immediate danger.

Before an impending storm, news stations will broadcast weather bulletins which include *watches* and *warnings*. They will describe the dangers and emergency procedures such as evacuations, etc.

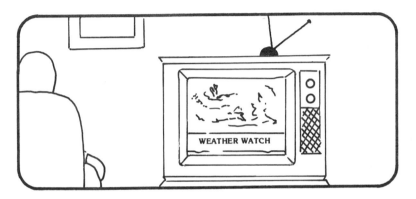

These *watches* and *warnings* are shown on your television screens on all channels. When the set is turned on they will apppear across the bottom of your screen stating whether its a *watch* or *warning*, a picture of what it is—for example, tornado, hurricane, thunderstorm, and the counties affected.

RADIO COMMUNICATIONS

Radio waves are a way that sound can be transmitted through the atmosphere. They travel at approximately the speed of light. Radio waves are somewhat similar to light waves. They can be reflected, absorbed, and blocked by steel buildings or large mountains. However, radio waves will penetrate nonconducting surfaces like wood or canvas, and can be transmitted and received quite clearly inside a house or in emergency shelters.

Radio waves on all frequencies can be received up to 100 miles away from a transmitter (sender). On certain frequencies, called medium and high frequencies, it is possible for radio waves to travel thousands of miles from the transmitter. They are actually reflected back to earth from the ionisphere from a distant transmitter. This would allow you to receive stations from hundreds of miles away while you cannot receive local radio stations.

OTHER EQUIPMENT

RADIO RECEIVERS (receive only)

As we have listed in Section SURVIVAL CACHE™, a very important part of your emergency preplanning is a battery-operated transistorized radio—AM/FM or just AM. If the power fails, you must have some form of communication with the outside; it might be your only source for information on the present danger. The Federal communications Commission (FCC) has assigned several broadcasting stations on AM and FM frequencies to stay on the air during widespread emergencies to broadcast information on what to do, where to go for help, and how to survive the local disaster. Even if you must go to an underground shelter, storm cellar, etc., AM radio waves should penetrate into that shelter sufficiently for good reception on your radio.

If your radio is for emergency use only, be sure to play it at least once every 3-4 months to be familiar with its operation. Practice turning it on, tuning it at night, and changing the batteries in the dark. Practice until you can change them quickly. Keep spare batteries near the radio and in your SURVIVAL CACHE™.

TELEVISION SETS

A television is also useful for staying up-to-date on local disaster news. Portable televisions that can run off 12 volt automotive power are also handy. This allows you to continue watching even if the power goes out. If you still have power after a disaster, your television should provide good coverage of what is happening and to what extent the damage is in your area. Try experimenting with the antenna lead-in wire for better reception. Your outside antenna may become damaged, but the lead-in wire, in many cases, can act as an antenna.

SHORTWAVE SCANNER RECEIVERS

Another type of receiver available is a scanner or shortwave radio set. The shortwave receives frequencies above the AM broadcast band. It will allow you to tune in reports from stations all over the world. Voice of America (VOA) broadcasts worldwide reports in English, and shortwave reception is easy with the built-in antenna or a small piece of wire attached to your shortwave receiver. Become familiar with your set and the most common frequencies in your area.

Scanner radios receive very high frequencies (VHF) and ultra-high frequencies (UHF). These channels are used by local law enforcement agencies. It is not illegal to own a scanner that listens in on the police and other emergency frequencies. Some states prohibit their use in the home or in an emergecy shelter. If you find the right channels, the scanner will allow you to stay tuned to local law enforcment and emergency medical agencies. If you are a radio buff, the scanner is just for you. It is a fascinating receiver that lets you hear all the action.

RADIO TRANSCEIVERS (send and receive)
No License Required

The word "transceiver" means a radio set that can transmit as well as receive. The tranceiver is built into one nice, neat package and simply requires the proper license and understanding on how to use it to communicate for help. The FCC makes several frequencies available for citizens in the United States to use to communicate with other citzens without a special license.

WALKIE-TALKIES

A very short range radio system that might be used to stay in touch around the house or with the neighbors is the portable 40 MHz walkie-talkies. They transmit with less than one watt of power, but this is enough to easily work around the house—and sometimes even down the block. You can buy pairs of these units on the same channel at almost every major discount store in the country. They are simply called "49 MHz walkie-talkies" and are usually priced under $100. Their range can be up to a block between two similar units.

COMMUNICATORS

Commmunicators are another short range type of communication device. These tiny radio transmitter/receivers operate up to a quarter-mile under good conditions from a headset and transmitter/receiver apparatus that you actually wear. The electronics clips on your belt, and the headset is worn with a small boom microphone next to your lips. When you talk, the unit automatically transmits. When you stop talking, you can receive other units on the same frequency. You buy your sets as a system. These communicators require no license, and must be ordered on the same channel to provide a complete communications system.

CITIZEN BAND (CB) RADIOS

A citizens band radio is a communications system that gives you the opportunity to contact others on the same radio system. CB radio may have a range of up to ten miles with a good outside antenna. A CB radio is ideal for the car to call out for help. There are portable CB's that may be used for calling out for help while mountain climbing or backpacking. There are CB base stations with outside antennas that will sometimes reach up to 40 miles. A CB radio is a good investment for safety communications because of the many CBers in your area that are on the air at any one time on the 40 allocated channels. It is estimated there are over 30 million operators in the United States.

CB equipment is available at almost every discount house, and the sets are "synthesized" for all channel operation. A good mobile unit might sell for under $100.00, complete with antenna system. You plug the power cord into the cigarette lighter, put the magnetic antenna on the roof, and you are on the air!

The key to good CB range is a well-elevated outside antenna. Signals travel line-of-sight. If you park your car on a high hill, you might be able to talk up to 100 miles away. Finding other radio operators on the air is easy—just turn through all the 40 channels until you hear a conversation loud and clear. Say, "Break, Break," in between the conversations, and chances are they will answer your call immediately. Channel 9 has been set aside as the national emergency channel in case you need to call for help. It is usually monitored by a volunteer group called REACT. All CB radios come with a detailed instruction book on how to operate the set, and how to use it to call for help. A CB radio is your best source for instant communications to others without requiring a license.

CB radios and the small 49 MHz communicators are your best value for localized communications. This equipment is available almost anywhere and installs in seconds.

RADIO TRANCEIVERS - License Required

MARINE AND AVIATION RADIOS

If you are a boater or small aircraft pilot, marine radio and aviation radio sets are available for local communications to authorities. The United States Coast Guard monitors specific marine VHF frequencies, mainly Channel 16 (156.800 MHz). The military and the Federal Aviation Administration (FAA) monitor the emergency frequency (121.5) for avionic radios, the standard broadcasting frequency for all emergency traffic and emergency landing transmitters (ELT's) for downed aircraft. A pilot, naturally, has been taught the use of radios, but as a nonpilot passenger this information could prove valuable.

If you are aboard a boat or in a plane with this type of equipment, it will allow you to communicate up to 100 miles away to local authorities for help. If you can not reach anyone on the emergency channel, simply turn the channel selector for any conversation in progress and interrupt the conversation when they pause with the words,"Break, Break" or "Mayday, Mayday." Even if you are not familiar with this type of radio equipment, you are bound to find someone on one of the channels so keep trying and then try to interrupt them to signal for help.

 Marine and aviation radios require licenses. However, there is no test involved; and if you have a boat or plane, licensing is easy.

GENERAL MOBILE RADIO SERVICE (GMRS)

Eight channels in the UHF band are set aside for citizens to use, called the General Mobile Radio Service (GMRS). This requires special FCC licensing, but no special test. This equipment is generally sold in pairs or as a system. You can operate locally between units up to 30 miles away, or through mountaintop repeaters up to 200 miles away. For the serious communicator, GMRS equipment at UHF is the way to go.

AMATEUR RADIO

If you are a Ham, amateur radio is ideal in an emergency. Ham radio operators pride themselves in providing emergency communications when all other radio services may fail. Amateur radio operators are trained in emergency communications and can always use your help. It takes approximately two months to pass your Amateur Radio license test. You need to know Morse Code as well as some theory to get your license. However, once you have passed the test and have your license, you can communicate all over the world or through local repeaters loud and clear with not-so-expensive equipment. The

Amateur Radio bands are always full of active communicators, so there is never a problem in signaling for help.

FOR TRANSCEIVERS

During an emergency you might come across an unknown piece of two-way radio equipment. If you must use the equipment to call out, first figure out how to turn it on. Like any normal radio, a click switch (toggle, dials) normally turns the set on and adjusts the volume. The knob that is called "squelch" should be rotated so you hear the background hissing noise. This allows you to pick up weak signals. Depress the "push to talk" switch, and clearly state your emergency and where you are. Then release the switch and wait for an answer.

You might have someone else move the antenna around to try for better reception. Have them move the antenna to a new position and then move away from the antenna before transmitting.

 DO NOT touch the antenna when someone is transmitting. If you have to handle it, make sure you are insulated (you can use a DRY heavy glove or thick cloth).

If the set is channelized, try different channels. You should be able to raise someone on this type of equipment. It might be on a business channel, or you might even have professional emergency communications units listening that will signal help for you.

Radio equipment is your lifeline to help in an emergency when your telephone fails. If your electricity goes off, your battery-operated radio gear still lets you know what is going on. Radio waves will penetrate through almost anything but a completely steel building. They can still get into that steel building by reflecting off windows and doorways. Radio waves are little affected by clouds and rain, so you still can get good reception during a storm.

It takes little skill to operate a transceiver-type radio. Turn it on, look for channel activity, and then intersperse a call for help when one radio operator is signaling to the other operator to go ahead and talk. Usually the words "Break, Break" are all that is needed to signal someone's attention.

For more information on radios, communications, and how to obtain licenses, check our Source Page for the leading authorities on the subject of your interest.

(Many thanks to Gordon West, WB6NOA, West Coast Radio School, for his invaluable assistance in providing detailed information on communications. VM)

SOURCE INFORMATION

For further information on the following subjects, write or call those listed. Most of these agencies have local offices throughout the country. Check your phone book for the listing nearest you.

Communications: Federal Communications Commission
or
West Coast Amateur Radio School
2414 College Drive
Costa Mesa, CA 92626
(714) 549-5000

Morse Code   Loraine McCarthy · WB6CIO
315 1/2 Ruby, Balboa Island, CA 92662
(714) 675-4415

First Aid Training/ American Red Cross
Information   American Heart Association

Food and   Food and Drug
related subjects: Administration

Disaster   National Flood Insurance Program
Insurance: Federal Emergency Management Agency
Federal Insurance Administration
Washington, D.C. 20745

Disaster   Civil Defense
Preparation: Department of Defense
National Address   Defense Civil Preparedness Agency
2800 Eastern Blvd., (Middle River)
Baltimore, MD 21220

Weather   National Oceanic and Atmospheric
Information: Administration (NOAA)

National Weather Service
U.S. Coast Guard

GEOGRAPHIC·SOUTH·POLE
AVERAGE TEMP MINUS 56°F
ALTITUDE 9186 ....
ICE THICKNESS OVER 9000 ....

ABOUT THE AUTHOR

Story of a Survivor

What's the real test — surviving the winter at the South Pole or lecturing to 30,000 elementary school children about how not to get lost? Viki Mason has done both – and a lot more. She is just as proud of the letters of thanks from school teachers and principles for her "Hug-A-Tree and Survive" assemblies as the special medal she received for her services to U.S. Scientists in the Antarctic.

From her first involvement as a troop leader and then teacher of survival skills to many Girl Scout Troups to her present activities with Saddleback Search and Rescue Team, Viki has been involved with wilderness safety education. A natural born fighter, she discovered that not all of the battles are against dangers in the wild. For three years she was on the board of directors for "Hills For Everyone," the organization instrumental in protecting 13,000 acres of wilderness from the intrusion of competing land developers. This area is now known as Chino Hills State Park.

If this seems like an "active life," she hasn't missed much. Mother of two children, her newest experience is being a grandmother. Although she enjoys the role, no one dares call her "Granny." What's this young grandmother doing now? Well, she is a successful businesswomen, Executive Director of Saddleback Search and Rescue Team, teaches "tracking" to police and sheriff's departments, certified Emergency Medical Technician, Emergency Services Officer-Sqd. 93-Civil Air Patrol, an amateur radio operator (N6EQF, Extremely Qualified Female), a scuba diver, a student pilot (both private and glider!), and, Oh Yes -an author.